THE LURE OF THE POND

Wallace Kirkland

THE LURE
OF THE POND

Illustrated by Eugene Karlin

HENRY REGNERY COMPANY   *Chicago*

This book is dedicated to Ethel

CONTENTS

THE POND

A pond is one of nature's crucibles. The water in it contains a segment of life's spectrum, both narrow bands of one-celled organisms and wider bands of creatures more complex.

There, penetrating rays from outer space unleash the basic elements to form some of life's simplest creatures. There, too, evolution can be seen at work; processes which took millenniums to perfect can be observed in moments of the present time. Tadpoles can be seen changing into frogs, and dragonflies emerging from aquatic nymphs.

And to a pond, as though revisiting a parent, come animals whose ancestors crawled out of primordial seas.

THE LURE OF THE POND

The Beginning

A narrow, winding road led up through a forest of naked trees disrobed by frost, and out upon a clearing. The land sloped gently downward to an abandoned cabin under a large poplar tree. Beyond it was a pond, winter-locked in ice. The brilliant midday sunlight of early March sparkled on a fresh fall of snow. In the distance was a wide expanse of marsh in which were whitened trunks of trees long dead. The left bank of the pond was once a cultivated field. Sumac and wild blackberry bushes now covered it. Along the right side was a tangled growth of willow and swamp maple trees.

Behind the cabin stood an outhouse, the door unhinged, and farther on there were the ruins of a barn. Gnarled, unkempt apple trees marked what had once been an orchard. Among the moss-covered rocks below them was a bubbling spring, the overflow trickling down through a deep ravine to feed the pond. Without the water from the spring there would have been no pond; no cabin, once a homestead, in the clearing.

Brown, tangled stalks of last year's cattails filled the near end of the pond. And in among them were the domes of several musk-rat houses. The new snow recorded tracks of recent visitors to the pond. Those of a rabbit who had been leisurely nibbling on the tops of weeds that stuck up above the snow. Later he had suddenly bounded off in long leaps toward the shelter of the woods. Tracks of a mink followed his, explaining the hurried departure. Among stalks of dry grass were feathery tracks of mice who had fed upon the seeds the grasses had produced. Those of a weasel entered a round hole in the snow out of which the mice had come. Close to earth and insulated by the blanket of snow was a dark winterworld inhabited by small creatures who do not hibernate. The weasel would find good hunting there.

Tracks of a fox led through a clump of willow and in among the muskrat houses. They showed where he had climbed a house and scraped the snow away. But many layers of roots and grass and cattail stalks, piled up laboriously last fall, and frozen solid, had kept the animals safe within their winter citadel.

At the base of the house was a yellow stain in the snow where the fox had lifted a leg and urinated. Not an act of frustration, but a sign to other foxes, both male and female, that he had passed that way.

His tracks led out across the frozen pond. Midway they turned at right angles in the direction of the woods, and near the shore blended with those of a smaller fox, probably a female, and, together, they continued on toward the marsh.

Walking out upon the ice, I was conscious of the varied forms of life in the depths below me—life active in the fish and small crustaceans. Life in the countless fertilized eggs of aquatic insects, and in the seeds of water plants. Life waiting for the warmth of spring to melt the ice, when the magic wand of the sun would again reach down and awaken the pond from its winter sleep.

How convenient if the magic sun could be selective, awakening only the "good" insects. But this is a mortal concept, for in the universal plan of life there is neither good nor bad. The "goats" as well as the "sheep" are awakened. And in the months to come swarms of the "bad" insects would be searching for my blood. For I had plans, when winter had vacated the cabin, to move in and spend the spring and summer months observing the wildlife associated with the pond.

As I continued across the pond, I was certain that curious muskrats would be investigating the sounds made by my footsteps. For they, like beaver, otter, and mink, can survive indefinitely under the ice, using a single lungful of air taken down with them. When the air needs renewing, they exhale in the water. It rises as tiny bubbles and collects as a large flat bubble against the underside of the ice. The carbon dioxide is mysteriously filtered out, and the animal refills its lungs with the original supply.

Also in the snow on the pond were the tracks left by deer that had frolicked there during the night. The moon had been full, and deer, like many other animals, including man, are strangely affected by moonlight.

At the far end of the pond was an ancient beaver dam. The animals that had built it to create the pond had long since been trapped for fur, but tracks indicated where two otters had recently crossed it. A patch of snow was rumpled in the abandoned field where they, like the deer, had stopped to play. With the otters this might have been a sign of mating madness, rather than the effect of moonlight. For March is the month when otters mate.

March is also the month in which the young are born, and by a cruel quirk of fate, the fur of the female otter is prime while she is nursing young. In Wisconsin, where the pond is located, the law permits otters to be trapped at that time of the year.

As I watch the otter tracks go up the slope and out of sight among the trees, I pray that the female of this pair, if she be a nursing mother, be not caught in a steel trap, leaving her young to die of starvation in their hidden den.

On the way back through the woods a barred owl hooted from the top of a tall dead tree. March is also the month in which owls mate, lay their eggs, and hatch their young.

To human thinking the nights of March seem long. But to an owl with young to feed they allow more time for hunting. In March, the leaves are off the trees, and the small animals upon which the owls feed can be seen more easily against the background of the snow.

From the abundance of tracks about the pond, I was confident that I, too, would have good "hunting."

Panning the Pond's Bottom

I moved into the cabin by the pond early in April. Eager to find out what the pond contained, I made a scoop of fine wire mesh, mounted it on the end of a long pole, dipped it far out in the water, and dredged a swath to shore along the bottom. I had a bucketful.

In it were the blackened leaves that had lain in the pond all winter: waterlogged sticks and bits of bark; sprouting moss and duckweed; and wisps of bright green algae. But also concealed in the muck were numerous examples of other living things.

Behind the cabin was an old galvanized washtub with circular ridges in the bottom. I turned it over and drilled rows of small holes between the ridges. The ridges served as the slats on the forty-niners' "shaker-board" against which the grains of gold collected when they panned the gravel in the California streams.

The "gold" I hoped to find against the ridges of my shaker-board was bits of living matter.

I spread a handful of my pond sample upon the washtub's bottom. As the water drained through the holes I searched for living "nuggets." Like the miner seeing the big one first, I picked up the most conspicuous, a three-coiled snail. The whorls in the shell spiraled counterclockwise from an umbilical center, which classified my specimen as a left-umbilical snail. I wondered how, when it began building its house of shell, it had remained true to its heredity and grown the coils so they circled to the left, for there are also right-umbilical snails.

Perhaps the snail had come out of the egg with the base of the shell it was to build upon already started, and all it could do was follow the established pattern. If this was true, if the way the spiral curved had been established in the egg, it had also determined the growth of the shell, just as red hair is determined in humans.

Putting the snail aside, I picked up a wet poplar leaf. On the back of it were clutches of snail eggs. They were globs of transparent jelly, resembling doll-sized gelatin shapes turned out of varying molds.

Out of a piece of wet moss an excited little creature emerged. His shell was like that of a shrimp. He swam on his side with rapid open-and-shut motions. I put him in some water collected in the cupped palm of my hand. Still swimming on his side, he circled this tiny pond, seeking a way out. From my book of pond life I identified him as *Gammarus fasciatus*, an amphipod. His common name is freshwater scud. Scud live on decayed matter, both animal and vegetable, and are very important links in the chain of balanced pondlife. A pair of these creatures, which mate and lay eggs from April to November, can produce 22,221 progeny in a single year! But they are a primary source of food for all the other pond creatures.

I filled a glass aquarium with pond water and placed my catch in it for further observation.

Under another soggy leaf I found a water spider. Her legs were drawn up close to her body, making her seem small. She was quite still, to avoid attracting attention. I put her in the aquarium, and, ladylike, she stepped daintily across the surface. Her feet made visible impressions on the water but did not break through

the surface; it was as though she was walking on tightly stretched transparent silk. She climbed up a piece of floating bark and, as I continued watching her, plunged off and tried to hide in the branches of a submerged water plant. But a film of air attached to the hairs of her body and legs enveloped her in a robe of shimmering silver and made her conspicuous among the green foliage of the plant. Such air, taken down with her, provides an underwater air supply, and she can remain there indefinitely.

Several whirligig beetles were collected in my scoop. I put them in the aquarium and they dashed about in wild concentric circles. One plunged to the bottom of the tank, taking with him a bubble of air attached to the tip of his body for his underwater supply. These creatures are gifted with two pairs of eyes, one pair for seeing below the surface, the other for seeing above. When handled, they exude a pleasant odor of musk.

A water-soaked stem of grass which I picked up seemed at first to have nothing on it. But under the hand lens I discovered a row of eggs that glistened as though they were pearls. Would that I had the occult power to gaze into their crystal depths and foretell what manner of creature was being created there. The fertilized egg is indeed a wondrous thing. Within its confines is a basic unit of immortality. Funneled into it by the union of male and female life forces is an infinite concentrate of all the biological past from which the creature comes. The process embodied in each egg glued to the stem of grass is identical to that in every incubating egg on earth, whether it is the egg of a snail, a freshwater scud, a frog, a spider, an insect, or a man. This is an axiom, a universal fact of life.

I added the spear of grass to the aquarium and hoped that I would see the eggs hatch.

Under a tuft of moss was a small, flat object that did not move. Held up against the light, it appeared translucent. It resembled a tiny, silken fan, with ridges like spokes radiating from a common center. The ridges were connected by a fabric of finely etched lines. The object was a scale from a carp. Each line denoted a period of time the fish had lived. They were like the annual growth rings on a tree, and by counting them under a microscope, it would be possible to tell the age of the fish from which it came. Every scale that grew upon that carp would have the same number of rings, but the pattern of no two would match. A challenging assignment for the designer of scales to see that no pattern is ever duplicated!

On the back of another leaf I found many wart-like bumps. I dissected one and found it empty. These were galls formed on the leaf last spring, when the sap was running high, by a sawfly that had punctured the leaf veins. At each puncture, a bubble of sap had formed and hardened. Within that bubble the female had laid her egg. The larva had fed upon the plant tissue, inside the gall, then spun a covering of silk. After metamorphosis, it had emerged as another sawfly.

Two white silken objects of tam-o'-shanter shape—the shape of the cap worn by Scotsmen—replete with tassels were attached to another leaf. They appeared to be the delicate work of spinning spiders but were the egg cases of a hydrophilic beetle. Each case contained more than a hundred eggs, but very few of the larvae hatching from them would live to become beetles. For while they are still in the larval stage, they feed upon each other and only the strongest survive.

Through the use of a hand lens, the rough surface of a piece of water-soaked bark is transformed into a region of mountains, valleys, and forests. Within the narrow confines of such a miniature world, innumerable creatures live out their span of life. Bark and all went into my storage tank for additional observation.

As I dipped from the pond, I caught a wet pussy willow bud

lying on the water's surface. Within its faded florets bright red hair-worms were living. When magnified, they became huge serpents, as though they were twining among the trees of a tropical forest.

There was a small snail I could not identify. His shell was pure white, not the usual mottled gray. I held him between thumb and forefinger and waited for him to crawl out. When he didn't move, I investigated with the dissecting needle. What looked like body was only mud. It was the shell of a snail long since dead, and the shell was whitened by exposure to the light.

Leaves that are rotting usually lie flat. I found one curled up and pried it open. Out of it wiggled a brilliant red-jointed worm, the larva of *Chironomus,* one of the midges. Searching out the Latin names in my pond book is as demanding an adventure as finding the owners. The Latin names are much longer than the creatures they identify. Most of the creatures are not big enough to rate a name of more than two or three letters. But the Latin names do suggest the work of many scientists who have labored through the years to put each creature in its proper class.

One glob of eggs puzzled me. The shape was different from any I had found. Two spots resembling eyes stared up through the lens of the magnifying glass. Then I detected a wiggle at one end of the glob, and it took on a familiar appearance. I had been finding so many new and different things that I failed to recognize the obvious. It was a pollywog. It was very small and would someday become a toad, not a frog.

A very active beetle crawled out of the muck. He resembled *Halipius ruficollis,* but I was not certain. I wrote him down as *Coleoptera,* and felt quite safe. This name covers all the beetles, and a hundred and fifty thousand of them have been identified.

A tiny, white speck, not much bigger than a pinhead, turned out to be a fingernail clam. It seldom grows to more than half an inch in length, despite the lengthy family name: *Sphaeriidae.*

A spider on a silken thread dropped down upon my notebook and slowly walked across it. Might she be snoopy, and was she trying to read what I had written? I speculated about drawing the image of a fly upon the paper, a fly so lifelike that the spider would be tempted to attack it. But even the cleverest of artists could not deceive her, despite the fact that she is nearsighted. Creating flies is not one of my attributes.

A dark object with two sharp, curved prongs intrigued me. Nothing in my book on ponds resembled it. I pulled it apart with the dissecting needle and discovered that, though it looked like a living creature, it was only the seed from a pondside burr.

Objects vegetable were available in abundance, too. I put a long, white thing in the palm of my hand and waited for it to make the motions of a worm. But like the burr seed, it did not move. I added several others to it, but there was no motion in them, either. I picked out another batch of the white threads and found two small leaves attached. They were the roots of duckweed, the smallest of flowering plants. The surface of the pond would soon be covered with them.

Then I found a long, white root that did move. The movements were very sensuous. It twisted and twined about itself as though trying to trade ends. The body was transparent, and I could see the movement of the digestive organs. The Latin name, *Chaetogaster diaphanus,* suggests such transparency. The common name is bristle worm. It feeds upon small crustaceans.

Another creature squirmed across the wet tin of my shakerboard. This one I knew. He was the larva of the dytiscus beetle, the underwater tiger, most vicious and bloodthirsty of all aquatic nymphs. The head and front part of his body suggested a centipede; his movements were those of a snake. Two feathery breathing tubes protruded to the rear. He was nearly two inches long. I picked him up, and he sank two sharp, sickle-shaped jaws deep into the flesh of my thumb. Through these he sucks the juices from his living prey: fish, tadpoles, crustaceans, nymphs, as well as members of his own species. I flung him from me, and he fell in the grass. I used tweezers when handling him the second time. In the aquarium he quickly captured *Gammarus fasciatus*, the amphipod I first put in. He hung on, below the water surface, sucking the juices, his body curved upward, and the "feathers" of his breathing tubes reaching up through the surface to obtain air.

Another nugget from the muck was the nymph of a dragonfly. This was a happy find. It was confirmation that in weeks to come, I would see the lovely creatures with the silvery wings emerging, through the miracle of metamorphosis, from just such unlovely nymphs. I put him in the aquarium, and he darted away, using his "jet propulsion" and sending a squirt of water skyward as his rear end disappeared below the surface.

Most of the solid matter from the bucket had now been panned, and only a few cupfuls of muddy water remained. It was swarming with minute living things. It would take hours to identify those I saw under my ten-power magnifying glass and years to identify the thousands more that a microscope would discover. The water in the pond was indeed a broth of life.

I poured the remaining water into the aquarium so that no creature would be spilled on the dry, inhospitable ground. As it flowed out, they tried in vain to swim against the current. Is this automatic resistance to violent change basic in the survival scheme?

A giant tank truck rumbled down the distant highway. I could see it passing through the leafless trees. Beneath its massive hood there was much activity: carburetors mixing fuel; pistons traveling up and down; valves opening and closing; plugs sparking in rhythm. Bound by the weight of his responsibility, the driver leaned upon the steering wheel and gazed at the road down which the man-made monster took him, a slave of the wheel. What a stark comparison, the truck and the life in the pond! There, in the quiet water, were countless living mechanisms, converting fuel into motive power far more efficiently than could be performed by the large and awesome truck.

There was much to be panned from the pond, but for the moment I had seen enough. I had "assayed" a generous sample and found evidence of "pay dirt."

The Path

Paths are symbolic of all living things. The earliest ones on earth were made by creatures crawling through the primordial ooze. Then, later, paths were made by animals in search of mates and food, and still later by man associating with his kind.

There are the migratory paths in the atmosphere traveled by the migrating birds around the globe. There are saline paths in the Atlantic that young eels follow from their spawning beds in the Saragossa Sea to the rivers in the Mediterranean from which their parents came. There are paths through the Pacific that salmon follow to the gravel beds from which they came as fingerlings. Feeding caterpillars follow paths of silk. Paths of sound are followed by crickets and mosquitoes; paths of light by mating fireflies; and sonic paths are used by bats to detect the flying insects upon which they feed. Graven in the biological memory of lemmings are the paths that lead them to destruction in the Arctic Ocean, seeking for a land which is no longer there. Moths, butterflies, and other insects find mates by following paths of scent. Airplanes speed along electronic paths, and man has spiritual paths he follows in his eternal search for God.

There is a path around the pond made by the feet of animals. It passes near the cabin door, winds among the grass and weeds down through the clump of willows. It crosses the stream that feeds the pond on a living bridge. This is a ten-foot section of tree trunk, placed there years ago.

First moss had grown along the prostrate trunk, then seeds blown by the wind had collected in the moss and germinated in the moisture. When the seeds' food-substance had been exhausted, their roots reached down and drew nourishment from the decaying log. Now out of it grow columbines, dandelions, birch and white pine saplings. And a path has been made through these growing things by the feet of the animals that have crossed the bridge.

The path then leads into the woods and comes out on the old beaver dam at the far end of the pond. From there it continues across the abandoned field, climbs the slope above the cattails, and joins itself beyond the cabin.

It is a magic path that leads into an enchanted world. When I step out of the cabin and follow it, I leave behind a world of pots and pans, of chairs and tables, of books and beds, and enter a world of the scent of flowers, the song of birds, the hum of insects. A world of spider webs outlined by drops of dew and of mounds of sand piled up by ants.

The path collects the autographs of the creatures using it. Some are boldly written, the footprints of a deer. Some are the signatures of lesser animals, raccoons, foxes, squirrels, rabbits, and skunks. Others are mere traceries left by the feet of little things, field mice, birds, and crawling insects. After a rain there always are the jumbled signatures of worms.

As I walk along the path, I look for friends. One is a rabbit, the last survivor of four that I found in a nest dug near the path and lined with the mother's fur. One by one they had disappeared, a meal for a weasel, a skunk, or an owl. The survivor likes to play along the path after the sun has risen, rather than be safely hidden in the weeds. He is the child that does not want to go to bed.

A female purple grackle, with a brood in a nest among the

vines on a dead poplar tree, beachcombs along the path for bugs and other things left stranded when the night tide retreated.

The male robin from the nest under the cabin eaves uses the path as a hunting ground. Keen-eyed, he stalks the earthworms that have come up to deposit their castings above the ground. Farther down the path another robin hunts. Each has his own territory, marked by a dividing line, invisible to me, that both birds respect.

One morning there was a feathered visitor. I had not seen his species here before. I heard his "bobwhite" call and hid behind the big oak tree to let him pass. He came quite close and gave his call again. This time the notes were slurred and sounded like "glog-white." Even a quail can be in bad voice at times.

Strange how we tend to give a human image to some of the sounds that birds and animals make. The "whippoorwill," the "ka-tydid," the "jug-o-rum" of the giant bullfrog. These are all in the English tongue. But the call of the redwing blackbird from the marsh has a foreign flavor. To me it sounds like the Mexican expression, "Okay keed, okay keed."

Along the path in early mornings are the mounds of sand built up by the ants during the night. They are evidence that below the ground's surface, out of sight, these highly organized creatures are busily producing eggs, tending their larvae, and storing food, so that the spark of ant-life they have inherited will be maintained.

The mounds resemble small arenas, high on the outside, low in the center, which mark the entrances to their galleries. How does the ant know just where to place each grain of sand that it is laboriously excavating, so that the mound will be symmetrical? Is the ant influenced by the North Star, whose orbit in the heavens, viewed from earth, is very small?

One morning, near one of the mounds I found the case of a large black beetle killed by a shrew. It was being carried along by rows of ants on both sides. Pallbearers taking it to a last resting place, their nest. Rather than leave it on the path to return to dust, the ants would make use of it for sustenance.

Another morning, I came upon a jumbled mound of sand also built up by ants. It looked more like the work of gophers. (Perhaps these ants had confused the North Star with the Milky Way!) The colony was "in swarm." Excited ants with wings were taking off to found other colonies. They were very clumsy fliers. (Wings do not normally belong on ants, as they do not belong on horses.) A light breeze blowing toward the pond carried many of the fliers with it. Some landed on the surface and were caught by feeding minnows. A ripple out on the pond marked where each ant had died. The elements that had been vitalized to create the ants, and used by them for building mounds, were being rearranged by death and used by fish for swimming.

Beside the path, in a smooth stretch of sand not far from where the ants were working, were several conical ant lion pits. Each pit was excavated by an insect's tossing out grains of sand with a powerful pair of jaws. The ant lion's common name is doodlebug, and he is the most patient member of the insect world. He lies concealed in the bottom of his pit and waits for food to come to him. His growth is measured not by time or the seasons but by the unwary ants and other crawling insects that stumble into his sandy trap.

Buried out of sight he cannot see his potential meal, but the dislodged grains of sand alert him. He responds by sending up a barrage of sand, which, like an avalanche tumbling down the steep sides of the pit, brings the victim to the bottom. The curved jaws dart out and close upon it, pull it struggling beneath the sand, and suck it dry. Then, with the jaws that excavated the pit and tossed the sand upward to bring the victim down, the empty carcass is thrown out upon the ground. The number of carcasses around the pit tells how well the ant lion is faring.

The ant lion life, which may last for many months if food is scarce, is merely the insect's larval stage of life, and the larva spends all its time feeding. When the larva has reached its full growth, metamorphosis takes over. The ant lion wraps itself in a cocoon of silk to which grains of sand attach themselves. When finished, it resembles a pellet dropped by a rabbit.

No greater opposite can be found than that between the ugly, bloodthirsty doodlebug with the powerful and vicious jaws and the frail, delicate, gossamer-winged creature that eventually emerges from the cocoon. It closely resembles a damselfly. And its life on earth is short. It does not eat. Its only reason for being is to find one of the opposite sex and mate. After mating the male soon dies. The female lives just long enough to lay her eggs, back in the sand, and thus to assure another generation of ant lions, who will dig their pits and spend their lives concealed in the bottom, waiting for food to come tumbling down.

I often sat beside the path and waited for an ant to stumble into one of the pits. I'd see it crawl over the edge and dislodge the sand that, like a burglar alarm, alerted the ant lion, then watch the barrage of sand tossed up by the unseen monster. The ant would try desperately to crawl back up, but seldom succeeded.

Each grain of sand was to the ant a head-sized boulder. Sometimes I'd rescue an ant before the fatal jaws closed on it. Most of the time I'd sit and watch the tragedy, trying to find a reason for it. None of this complicated method of killing made sense to my human thinking. Ants have their use on earth as scavengers. A colony living under the cabin helped keep my floor and table clean. And bees and other flying insects are important agents in pollinating flowers. But the final stage of the ant lion is too delicate for this. Why were countless ants and other insects sacrificed to provide so inadequate a creature with a brief moment of sexual activity?

"And God made the beast of the earth after his kind, and cattle after their kind, and every thing that creepeth upon the earth after his kind: and God saw that it was good."

The seasonal succession of flowers growing along the path suggests the plantings of a wise gardener, who sees that there is always something blooming for the insects to feed upon. The annual surge of flowering begins when winter's chamberlain, Jack Frost, is still about. It comes into full bloom when he departs and continues unbroken until he returns at the end of summer to spread his hoary blanket over the soil and reclaim it for his master.

Trailing arbutus is the first flower to arrive. While patches of snow still lie on the hillside beneath the oaks, its tiny blossoms, held close to earth and protected by the hairy leaves, defy the cold. If flower scents were visible, a shell-pink mist would be seen enveloping every arbutus plant.

Hepaticas are other flowers that arrive while Jack is still about. Their hairy stems are insulation against the cold, and they do not wait for leaves. One morning I found one that had pushed its budstem up through a hole in a fallen oak leaf. The flower opened with the leaf still around the stem. I thought of a pilgrim with neck fast in stocks being chastened for his forwardness.

The pussy willows also challenge Jack's domination. They provide the first source of nectar for the insects that have survived the winter on stored food.

The skunk cabbage, like the hepatica, does not wait for leaves. The phallic-sculptured spathe pushes up through the bare black earth. Leaves quickly follow, as though in haste to conceal the putrescence of the flower's odor, which is not affected by environment. These plants grew at both ends of the pond. Those growing beside the clear water where the spring flowed in stank just as much as did the ones growing in the black mire of the marsh.

Yellow clusters of marsh marigolds are chandeliers that light up the moist area before the other vegetation comes.

Spiderwort, "holding its blooms aloft like clustered stars of blue," grows in profusion between the path and the pond. This flower cannot stand the heat of day, and if I am late on my morning walk, I find the petals closed.

And this one needs no insects in its propagation. The stamens are delicately balanced. The slightest breath of wind sets them in motion, and they scatter their male grains of pollen on the receptive female parts. The blue petals, with their golden-veined beauty accentuated by early morning drops of dew, become a fitting backdrop for the creative dance of the stamens.

Sweet clover, unlike spiderwort, depends upon bees for its fertilization. Tall clumps of it grow along the path in the abandoned field. The blossoms are small, and at a passing glance seem insignificant, but they distill a heady perfume that makes up for their lack of size.

This perfume gives a feeling of delight when inhaled by human nostrils and creates a scented path that the bees can follow to the source of the nectar. When the flower bud first appears, the pistil is confined within a sheath, under spring tension. A bee's tongue probing for the nectar touches a trigger that releases the spring. The pistil springs erect, scattering grains of pollen on its liberator. These are then carried by the bee to the adjoining flowers, cross-fertilizing them, making payment for the nectar it has received. If the pistil is not released, the flower withers. Without the assistance of the bee there would be no sweet clover.

White trillium grow along the path where it winds through the woods. These get their flowering done before the new foliage of the trees above them cuts off the sunlight. The flower stalk is weak and wobbly when the bud unfolds. It's like the neck of a newborn baby, which cannot support the head. But in a day the stem gets strong and holds the lovely white flower aloft. A clump of them resembles a patch of last winter's unmelted snow.

The bellwort flower, on the other hand, never holds its head erect. A bee must hang upside down on it to collect the nectar.

At the edge of the woods I see the first dandelion, and on it is a matriarchal bumblebee. The lone survivor from the summer, she will now seek out the abandoned nest of a field mouse, or an excavation in a decayed log, and in it deposit her eggs. And from them will come this year's colony.

The color of the infant maple leaves as they uncurl in spring is just as brilliant as that of the leaves in fall. But this is the color of youth. In the fall it denotes age and death.

Patches of the white Juneberry flowers among the darker evergreens suggest snow. The petals floating through the woods are like falling snowflakes.

Four kinds of violets grow in the wooded shade: shy white ones, bird's foot, a large yellow species, and the vigorous common blue-violet.

Compass plants are everywhere. Their long, narrow leaves standing upright, the edges pointed north and south, the flat sides east and west. The chlorophyllic "compass" in this plant is activated by the sun and not affected by the earth's magnetic lines of force.

Fox droppings, often seen along the path, contained the hair and bones of field mice. And there were many miniature ponds in the low places in the woods, some just a few feet wide. Swarms of mosquitoes rose from them in early spring. They seemed to be hurrying to get their larval state completed before the water evaporated.

One morning, in the abandoned field, I saw the sunlight glistening on a mass of iridescent bubbles high up on a sweet clover plant. I spread the mass apart and found a small green creature with a boat-shaped body and two large eyes set wide apart. His beak was buried in the clover stem out of which he was sucking the sap. The other end was swinging in a rhythmic motion from side to side, and at the end of each swing a bubble formed and adhered to the adjacent ones, creating the glittering mass that, moving along his body, soon covered him. Sometimes a bubble got too big and burst.

The physical me, despite the urge, is far too big to crawl inside the crystal house, but there is a mental me that has no limitations. It knows no distance far or near, no size, no time. The past, the present, and the future all unite in it.

This mental me went into the house and found itself surrounded by a thousand rainbows as the sunlight shone through the translucent bubble covering. And the temperature inside was cool, for bubbles filled with air make good insulation.

Would that I had the power to suck sap from sweet clover plants and with it build a crystal house. To me this tiny creature is a thing of wonder, but to a farmer raising sweet clover to feed his cows it is just a common spittlebug, a pest to be destroyed by modern insecticides.

Another morning on the path in the abandoned field I came upon a painted turtle laying eggs. I was reminded of a night on Key Marquesas, beyond Key West, where I had seen a giant hawksbill turtle laying hers. The moon was full, the sea a sheet of yellow glass. She came in on the rising tide, her enormous head breaking the surface a few yards out from shore, and the pent-up air in her lungs was expelled in one tremendous gasp. I crouched and watched her lumber up across the white sand. The moonlight shining on her sea-encrusted shell enveloped her in a phosphorescent aura. She was like an apparition from another world. In the low scrub growth above the high-tide mark she dug her nest. Her two hind flippers, used as humans use hands, worked in perfect rhythm as they scooped out the sand. When the hole was deep enough, a tube extended from her anus, and the eggs came out in bursts, like bullets from a machine gun. When they had all been deposited, she pushed the sand back with her flippers, then dragged her cumbrous body in wide circles over the spot to camouflage it.

Though many miles apart, and of different size and species, the two turtles had egg-laying procedures that were identical. Both of these creatures dug their nests and laid their eggs while in a seeming coma. While they were in the trance, an involuntary power had directed the process. Never once did they turn their heads to see what they were doing. The painted turtle laid only ten eggs, the hawksbill, a hundred and sixty-five.

The next morning when I reached the spot where the painted turtle had deposited her eggs, there was an empty hole. Scattered about it were the shriveled shells of broken turtle eggs. The tracks left in the sand were those of a skunk. During the night the fertile eggs that were intended to have carried on the life stream of the painted turtle had been appropriated for the life stream of a skunk.

One midday, as I walked along the path, two beady eyes peered at me from a newly dug hole in the hard earth. I used my camera case as a stool and watched. The eyes retreated down the hole, and a burst of sand came out. It was a hunting wasp digging a hole in which to lay her egg. As she excavated sand, she made a loud buzzing noise with her wings, evidently to scare away parasitic flies. When the hole was deep enough to suit her purpose, she flew away, but not before she smoothed the heaps of sand about the hole so it would not be conspicuous. In half an hour she returned, dragging a caterpillar between her legs, and pulled it headfirst down the hole. On this she would lay her egg.

The activity had seemed relatively simple: an insect digging a hole and putting a caterpillar in it to feed the larva that would hatch from the egg.

But there is a thing about these hunting wasps that challenges the power of human reasoning. It is too elusive to be seen under microscopes, or examined in test tubes, and cannot be explained as instinct, natural selection, or survival of the fittest. It savors of Tennyson's "The Great Intelligencies Fair that range above our mortal state." We see it working, but we don't know how it works.

The caterpillar that the wasp had captured seemed quite dead, but it would remain alive for many days, until the larva hatched to feed upon it. Though the parent wasp is a vegetarian, living on the juices of fruits and flowers, the larva must have living food. It cannot survive on corpses.

When the wasp had found the caterpillar host, she had injected an anesthetic into it. Not with random pokings of her stinger, but, like a doctor with an X-ray chart to guide him, she had carefully inserted her "needle" into each segment of the caterpillar, paralyzing the bodily movements, but not the jaw muscles. It still could bite. To stop this action, the wasp had used her mandibles, crushing the cranial nerve by degrees, a small squeeze at a time, until movement ceased. Had she been careless in this final operation—bitten too hard and severed the nerve—death would have resulted, and the caterpillar would have been no good for larval food.

The wasp took off to locate other caterpillars, and I gave up the vigil, but, before leaving, I pushed a small stick in the ground to mark the spot. When next I passed there, the hole was covered, and bits of grass were spread around as camouflage. It was a more sophisticated job than either turtle had used to camouflage her nest. Had it not been for the marker stick, I could not have found it.

I often detected the slithery track left by a snake around the pond. It indicated where the snake had crossed the path, moving toward the pond for frogs, and again where he had recrossed it, full-bellied, on his way to the woods to digest his meal.

One day I saw him. Although I knew that sometime we would meet, the sight was startling. I shuddered. I had been watching an orchard oriole weave her pendent nest on the low, overhanging limb of an oak. I turned to walk away, and there lay the snake upon the path. He was five feet long. He looked at me through cold and lidless eyes, his forked tongue darting in and out as he picked up the vibrations I had caused. Cutting a forked stick from a hazel bush, I pinned him to the ground. I grasped him just behind the head, but too far back, and in a movement too fast for me to respond to he struck the forefinger of the hand that held him. I let him go.

Two drops of blood oozed from the holes his fangs had made. I sucked them and spat out the bloody saliva. Two such pinpricks from the wrong kind of snake could bring death to a man made in the image of God. But he was the right kind, and the twinges of pain in my shoulder that I felt later on were caused, I knew, by fear.

A water moccasin sunbathed on a partly submerged log near the silver birch. On my walks around the pond I would have fun stalking him. I counted the stalk successful if I reached the shelter of the birch before he saw me. When there were turtles sunning on the log, I never got that close. Their keen eyes would discover my movements when I was still far away, and they would plop into the water and warn the snake.

He came to an ignominious end, for a water snake. He drowned. I had set a transparent plastic trap for minnows at the deep end of the pond. The trap had an inverted funnel at one end. The snake crawled in and could not find his way out. He was dead when I pulled up the trap, his belly full of minnows.

Late one afternoon I sat upon my camera case beside the path where it wound through the darkest part of the woods, down near the pond, and watched a crayfish building his "chimney," the land entrance to his underwater tunnel. He had just started to work above the ground when I first arrived. He came up through the moist black earth, carrying a ball of it between his two enormous fighting claws. Using the claws as hands, he spread the soil around the hole to form the base of the chimney. He then backed down the hole and after several minutes came up with another armful.

The claws he was using were designed for fighting and not for spreading mud, and they were very clumsy tools with which to work. They had been developed in a dim, ferocious past to protect him against his enemies. They reminded me of the mechanical arms now being used by man for handling objects in atomic furnaces, arms developed in the sophisticated present to protect man from a power that he, through knowledge, has released and which, uncontrolled, could annihilate him.

The claws of the crayfish and the natural arms of man are manipulated in the same manner, by nerves and muscles coordinated in the brain. Both species are capable of waging war. But intelligence has entered the development of man, and because of it, his arms and fingers can be used to play a violin, paint a picture, remove a damaged fragment from a human brain, and fondle a woman. These things the claws of the crayfish cannot do. It is doubtful that the newly developed robot arms of man, sophisticated though they are, will ever be able to do all of them either, nor fondle a woman ever.

It is easier to comprehend the life processes in the soft-bodied creatures, caterpillars, birds, fish, mammals, than in those, such as the crayfish, covered with hard outer shells. They appear more like machines with joints that need lubrication.

The crayfish is an amazing creature which has survived from a far distant past. It thrives on a variety of foods—vegetable, carrion, living creatures—and can make a meal out of its own discarded shell. It replaces the shell when it gets too small, and can replace claws that are broken off. It has an ingenious way of communicating with other members of its kind. Through ball-and-socket joints at the base of its long feelers, it can transmit signals, audible in the larger species to man, that tell of locating food, as well as warn of danger.

All of this is "standard equipment" and arrives with the young crayfish from the "egg factory." How wonderful it would be if human engineers could design an automobile capable of using such a wide variety of fuel, of replacing parts when they are damaged, and at regular intervals of producing a whole new outer covering. And yet it is not so. Indeed, while a modern automobile has over twenty thousand separate parts, a vastly greater number are needed to produce a crayfish. It is a sobering thought to realize how limited some of man's achievements are.

As I watched the crayfish in his prehistoric armor back down into the dark tunnel, I thought of the air-raid shelters now being built by human beings.

I left the crayfish still working at his chimney-building. By the following morning the chimney was nearly a foot in height, and several others had been built in the marsh area during the night.

The Bumblebee

The bumblebee was the most primitive and archaic type of insect that visited the pond. Unlike the honeybee, the species is not highly organized. Only the queen of the last year's colony survived the winter. She hibernated inches below the frozen surface of the ground. A unique insect antifreeze solution kept the liquids in her body from freezing and causing death. She had mated at the end of summer and carried through the winter the fertile eggs upon which the future of her heritage depended. When she crawled out of the ground with the first warm days of spring, her every action suggested an urgency to get the eggs deposited.

The first few days were spent in consuming great quantities of nectar. The early catkins of the pussy willows provided most of this. Then she spent hours flying in circles low above the ground, searching for a convenient cavity in which to start her nest. Unlike the highly organized honeybee, the bumblebee does not construct a permanent comb of wax. It is obliged to start anew each spring. The cruising queen would alight at every promising opening and carefully examine it. When she had located a suitable place, she minutely established the location so she could recognize it when she returned.

All bumblebees follow the same routine in doing this. On their first flight they rise in a tight spiral above the spot, recording the prominent landmarks, a weed, a stone, a bunch of grass. These are recorded in the comparatively few available memory cells in their brains. On their return, for the first few flights, they follow the spiral down. As the number of their flights increases, they are able to zero in on a direct line without the use of the spirals. (Experiments have been made by removing obvious landmarks, then noting the confusion caused when the bumblebee returned.)

As soon as the queen has collected sufficient food, she presses her body down against the floor of the nest and exudes flakes of wax from between the plates on her underside. She then constructs a single honeypot near the entrance and fills it with pollen and nectar. This is to provide her with a food supply while she is brooding and on days when the weather is inclement. She then presses out more wax and builds another cell, this one to hold the eggs. A small supply of pollen is stored in it for the larval food, and in it she lays eight to a dozen eggs. The cell is sealed, and in between her flights for gathering food she keeps her body close against it to help with the incubation.

In hives of honeybees there is no need for this maternal care. They long ago have solved the problem of the proper temperature for incubation.

The eggs of the bumblebee hatch out in four or five days. The larvae feed at first upon the food stored in the cell, but as they grow and need more food, the mother pierces the cell wall and injects a fluid of honey mixed with pollen. In seven days their larval period ends, and each one spins a yellow cocoon of silk in which to pupate. They have no further need for food, and the queen constructs additional cells and lays more eggs.

The honeybee has solved the problem of spinning cocoons. The larvae are fed at first in the open cell, and when they are ready to pupate, their cells are capped with wax, and they are sealed in. Later they emerge as fully developed bees.

In twelve to twenty days—it depends upon the weather—the new bumblebees emerge. Their first act is to clean off their antennae and legs and then to visit the honeypot that the queen has constructed and filled. After three days they start out to collect nectar and pollen and begin to assist the mother with rearing the subsequent groups as they arrive.

The surplus food brought in is stored in empty larval cases and additional honeypots are built. The honey of the bumblebee is heavier than that of its useful honeybee cousins. But the production of it is not as highly organized and no great quantities are produced.

The first batch of bumblebees to emerge resemble the mother, but due to the inadequacy of the early spring diet, they are smaller. As they increase in number, they take over the provisioning of the colony. The queen is then confined to the nest and keeps on laying eggs. The workers last about a month. They die from overwork and are constantly being replaced by new ones. A thriving colony will contain as many as three hundred at its peak.

The early bumblebees are sexless, neuters. Later in the season, when there is much nectar, the larvae are fed abundantly. Some develop into females with functioning ovaries; others into males. Unlike the honeybee, the mating of the bumblebee doesn't take place high in the air after a frantic chase of the queen by many drones. Male bumblebees lie in wait on bushes and pounce upon any female coming within their line of vision.

The queen that started the colony doesn't live through a second winter. She sometimes dies before the summer ends. She is then replaced by one of the many queens in the area. At summer's end all but the pregnant females perish. With the coming of frost, they bury themselves in the ground and hibernate, then come out in spring to start the bumblebee cycle of life all over again.

The Spoor of Life

On a warm and sunny afternoon in early April, I lay stretched out upon my back on the sloping hillside above the pond, under a black walnut tree. Last summer's crop of leaves lay inches deep around me. Having been held down by winter snows and beaten by the rains of spring, they were tightly packed. The sunshine lay upon them as it had when they were on the tree. But absent was the green chlorophyll needed to trap the energy from the sun's rays, the energy that is vital to the mysterious process of photosynthesis, which is the source of all living matter and of all biological energy on earth.

Without leaves, there would have been no black walnut on the sloping hillside, no human being resting beneath, for life in me, as well as that in walnuts, depends upon the work of leaves. They are the "silver cords," umbilical in function, which bind all life to earth. Were these cords "loosened," and all leaves destroyed, life would depart, as it had done from the leaves which surrounded me, and the earth would once again be sterile.

The fallen leaves were but the spoor of life, showing where life had passed. Now, through decay and the activity of worms, they were once again becoming part of the soil, taking with them substance gathered from the sun while they were still living.

This would enrich the soil, returning with interest the loan of the elements borrowed from it the spring before.

Some of the minerals that had fallen back with the dead leaves would again become parts of future leaves upon the tree. But in the scheme of life, where constant rearranging is the norm, a leaf does not sink into the earth as a leaf, then as a leaf arise and fasten itself to the same twig from which it fell. And while the leaves were being returned to earth, the naked tree awaited, in the warm expectancy of spring, another crop of leaves about to take their places.

It is a wanton waste to use a leaf for just one season and then to discard it. It seems the caprice of a timeless power, capable of producing leaves at will. Perhaps the beauty of the annual cycle makes up for this waste. The delicate buds unfurling in early spring; the full-formed leaves stirred by the summer breezes; the brilliant color display of fall. But vain indeed is he who thinks that the scheme of life for leaves was planned for his enjoyment.

A leaf is a very complex thing. It must contain chlorophyll to trap the energy from the sunshine. It also must have many pores through which excess water sent up by the roots may evaporate. Its many veins must all connect, through stem and branch, with the supply lines in the bark. There must be a functioning pipeline from the smallest vein in the highest leaf to the tiniest rootlet sunk deep in the earth. And the new leaves on the black walnut would possess all these wonders.

I picked up a leaf and examined it. The intricate network of the ribs and veins stood out in bold relief against the faded background. I examined other leaves and compared their outlines. No two leaves are alike.

If all the leaves from the tree were fed into a modern computer, one capable of comparing their outlines, would there be two whose every notch and every point matched, perfect copies? If perchance two such were found, then segments of their rib and vein structure would be different. There is a family resemblance, and each of the leaves can be identified as coming from a black walnut, but each is different, too.

It is intriguing to realize that the patterns of the different shapes of leaves are contained within the seed which produced the tree. The outlines were not left to chance. But what first determined their shapes? Hardly spots turned up on cosmic dice.

Leaves are the spoor of life and owe their homage to the sun. So does a part of me. But I like to think there is another part of me which is the "spoor" of a Great Intelligence, to whom the sun owes homage.

Unless this is true, I am fixed, like that black walnut on his peculiar spot, to grow, draw nourishment, propagate, and rot.

The Robins

Because of a pair of mated robins, I was spared the work of cutting firewood for the kitchen stove. The former tenant left a bucksaw hanging on a wooden peg under the eaves on the rear wall of the cabin. The robins' nest of mud and straw was built upon the peg, and the bucksaw became part of the support. To move the saw would have wrecked the nest. I bought a load of wood, already cut, from a farmer who owned a power saw.

The robins' nest was built on top of one that was used last year. For these two birds, the cabin was their goal when they migrated north. The old nest could have been his, or hers, but I liked to think that it had belonged to both of them, that they had returned, a mated pair, to raise another brood.

How did the pair of robins find their way when they flew northward with the spring? By what method of reckoning were they able to locate this small spot in the vast area of many states? On the northward trek, they had passed many other good nesting sites with sheltering eaves. But they had kept flying until they reached this one, and there they had built their nest.

A ship at sea is steered by readings taken through a sextant on the sun and stars. An airplane follows an established electronic path. An instrument on the panel informs the pilot when he is in tune with it. When salmon hatch, the chemistry peculiar to the water becomes a part of their biological memory. Later, when the urge to spawn comes upon them in the ocean, they swim along the coast until they encounter the water from the stream in which they hatched. Being attuned to its chemical path, they follow it to the original spawning gravel that they had left as fingerlings.

The robins did not have instruments of brass and lenses with which to guide themselves by the stars. Nor did they have transistors for tuning into preestablished paths. Like the salmons', theirs was a biological guidance system, dependent upon chemical secretions in their bodies. Their navigation was tied in with several factors: the periods of sunlight, the magnetic lines of force, the pull of gravitation, and, perhaps, the forces, yet unnamed, from outer space. All these combined to produce a special atmosphere, which varied with the seasons and the geographic locations. When they "matched up" their biological pattern with this, they felt "in tune," and kept in tune by following it. They "felt" their way north. The combination of all these variables produced a pattern in the area about the cabin that was unique to it. In it they felt "at home."

The changing pattern of the season, the lengthening hours of daily sunlight, triggered the production of sex hormones in the birds. Eggs began forming in the female ovaries, and sperm was produced in the testes of the male. The first indication of the rising surge of sex was in their vocal sounds. Subtle inflections in the calls of each were heard. The new tones in the cries of the female stimulated desires in the male. His responses stimulated her, too. When these desires reached full development, the urge for physical contact necessary to send the sperm on its journey to fertilize the eggs came. Elaborate biological plans had evolved through the ages for accomplishing this act. The rising urge of sex within the bodies was transferred to the senses of sight and hearing. Here they could be observed. For many months the pair had associated with themselves and others of their own species. The only way the sexes could be told apart was by their size and coloring or by anatomical investigation. Drab color in the female; red breasts in the male. Then had come the outward indications of the rising inward surge of sex: the subtle inflections added to their voices, the differing postures. If all the feathers had been absent from both birds at this period, the sexes could have been differentiated by their sounds and actions.

Then the male began chasing the female, and she avoided him. This, too, intensified desire. When desire reached its climax, the female let herself be caught, assumed the accepting squatting posture, which the male recognized, and they mated. For posture, as well as tone of voice, is important in communication between birds.

Next, in some mysterious manner, the female became aware that preparations must be made to receive the eggs. There are many different ways in which creatures who lay eggs prepare for their arrival. An innate something in them tells them when the eggs are due. Spiders weave silken sacs; bees and wasps make cells of paper, wax, or clay; fish scoop out nests in gravel; sawflies sting plants and produce galls of sap; turtles dig holes in the sand. Birds build nests.

Perhaps the activity of the sex hormone creates the urge to build the nest. But who is the architect that directs the selection of the site, the collecting of the building materials, and the construction itself? There must be a different one for each kind of bird. A robin always builds a robin nest. It is not an imitation of the other birds' nests. The outside is reinforced with straw and clay; the lining is of soft material.

Whenever I watch a bird building a nest and see it pause on the edge with a mouthful of new material, I wonder if it is waiting for some special guidance on just where to place it.

The method of navigation can be explained. We can understand the sperm's entering an egg, the cells' dividing and multiplying to form the new creature. But the why and how of nest-building is a mystery.

The completed structure is evidence that the architectural advice the bird received was adequate. The nest will serve her purpose both in size and shape. The timing, too, is right. It is finished when she is ready to move in and lay her eggs.

The female robin was already sitting on her nest when I moved into the cabin. My sudden appearance as I walked around the corner of the cabin startled her. When she suddenly left the nest, just a few feet from my head, she startled me. We both made involuntary vocal sounds. Her mate interpreted the ones she made and came flying in to investigate. Another human being hearing mine would have known by them that I, too, had been startled. The basic sounds, fear, threat, surprise, contentment, which animals, including man, make, become a universal language understood by all. Such sounds were made by man before he invented the use of words.

During my first days at the cabin, the female left the nest whenever I came in sight. Then, as she got to know me better, she remained on the nest while I moved about. Here was evidence of communication between us. Do we emanate a substance, perhaps in the form of vibrations, or as a pheromone, which other animals can detect? At any rate, animals know whether the approach is a hostile or a friendly one. The saying, "It's funny what you see when you don't have a gun," does have a basis in fact.

The days spent in incubating the eggs were good ones for the robin. Her northern flight had ended, she had found her mate, built a nest, and laid her eggs. Now she could sit upon them and relax. Three or four worms a day sufficed for food, and worms were plentiful. The male seemed to enjoy the days, too. At daybreak and at nightfall he would perch high in the white birch tree and sing.

But there was no relaxing inside the eggs. In them the miracle of creation was in full swing. Cells were dividing, creating new ones, following an intricate pattern of organization. Some were developing into brain, others into bone and muscle, some into skin and the intestinal tract. The beak and vocal cords were being assembled. The eyes were being located in their proper places. Special cells were grouping to form the retinas. Organs were being produced. A heart was being joined to a network of arteries, veins, and capillaries. An intricate system of nerve fibers was reaching out and establishing contacts.

The end result in each egg would be a new functional creature, a robin, with a family resemblance to the female sitting on the nest and to her red-breasted mate up in the white birch tree.

While these forces of creation were silently at work in the feathered warmth beneath her, the female sat as though in an easy chair, oblivious of them.

One morning there was a new reaction to my presence. Instead of sitting still when I came into sight, the female hurriedly left the nest, and there were obvious notes of concern in her cries. Soon she was joined by the male, and they flew about excitedly. One of the eggs had hatched during the night. In the nest was a living thing, and in their biologically based training they were responsible for its protection.

The act of hatching from the hard-shelled egg is not a simple matter. The embryonic position of the beak makes it impossible for the chick to peck its way out. A special muscle has been designed to accomplish this. It is a "hatching" muscle, powerful enough to flip the beak against the shell with sufficient force to crack it. That such a muscle was designed for this sole purpose is evidenced by the fact that soon after the shell-cracking is completed, the muscle atrophies.

Human beings who observe wildlife often become anthropomorphic, likening the activities of creatures, especially where a mated pair with young are involved, to behavior in mankind. We tend to speak of them as sweethearts, husband and wife, and of the young as children. When we see the male robin offering a worm to the female seated on a nest, he appears to be a gallant gentleman presenting a dainty morsel of food to his lady. He almost bows courteously as he does so. Perhaps some truth lies behind it all. But perhaps it is we who are like creatures, not they like humans.

During the first days after the eggs hatched, the female spent most of her time upon the nest, and the male brought her food. He had a set manner of approach, landing first upon a limb of the white birch tree, the worm held by one end, squirming in his beak. Then, like a ventriloquist, without opening his mouth he made sounds, informing the female of his presence. She answered him, indicating that she was aware he was near. He then flew to a rung of a ladder hanging against the wall, hopped from that to the frame of the bucksaw and finally to the peg around which the nest was built. The female didn't reach out for the worm, but, like a decorous lady, opened her mouth as he placed her food into her beak.

Then she stood on the edge of the nest, and four heads sprang up in the air. Four yellow, V-shaped mouths spread wide, and though their eyes were not yet opened, four young robins expected to be fed. With four such similar chicks, the female somehow knew which one to feed. Perhaps the sounds of a fed robin are different from those of a hungry one.

After feeding her young, the female settled on the nest and tucked the small heads back under her feather covering. Usually, the male waited until she had disposed of the worm, as though he did not trust her and wanted to make sure she didn't eat it. I consoled myself with the thought that he stood there only to admire his offspring.

Full-grown creatures live by the laws of the solunar rhythm. This rhythm, which corresponds to the daily movement of tides and, like them, is caused by the attraction of sun and moon, can easily be observed at back-yard feeding stations. The feeder will be full of food, the birds perched in the trees about the area, none of them feeding. Then, quite suddenly, they get active, and all begin to feed. This activity lasts for an hour or even less, and then the birds stop and do not feed again until the next period arrives.

There are two such periods a day, but the rhythm did not apply to the young robins, who, because of their rapid rate of growth, had insatiable appetites.

When their eyes had opened, the young became conscious of my presence, and when I approached the nest, they crouched down to make themselves less conspicuous. When they had grown their feathers, there was no room in the nest for the female. She no longer sat on them, but roosted on the wooden peg. One morning, as I walked toward the nest, they took off in a scattering burst of flight. One landed in a low sumac bush; three flew toward the white birch tree. Two of them reached it; the other fell in the grass and lay there helpless with wings spread. I picked him up and put him back in the nest. He tried again, and that time landed in the birch tree.

This innate ability for flight is amazing. The young robins were able to manipulate their wings without having lessons or practice. This skill must have been incorporated in the yolk of each blue egg and transmitted to the brain as it was formed. The proof that such a flying pattern existed was demonstrated by the birds' ability to fly.

Within a day, three of the young had left the area. I found the fourth one in a clump of weeds near the ruins of the old barn. The mother was feeding him. She would fly down near him with a worm and make sounds in her throat. He would come out of the weeds making fretful noises like a spoiled child and wait for her to put the worm in his mouth. He was probably the one who had missed the tree on his first flight, the weakling of the four. Surely he was doomed to become food for a weasel or a skunk and never to live to make the long trek south.

But in my anthropomorphic thinking, I was comforted in thinking that mother love in robins did exist, and that the female robin was doing her maternal best to see that the weakling of her brood survived.

The Feel of Life

Early one morning I crushed a newly emerged dragonfly between my thumb and forefinger and felt its life depart. I had held a living creature, in which a heart was circulating blood, a brain was coordinating a network of nerves and muscles, and two eyes were capable of sight. When I began to squeeze, there was a struggle. Groups of cells resisted the violent change. Then the struggle ceased, and with the dragonfly's death I held between my fingers a green pulpy mass with only the wing recognizable. In this dead mass were all the basic elements that had been carefully arranged to create the dragonfly. No single one was missing. But the thing we call life had left them. And I had felt it go.

This was not an act of wanton destruction, but of euthanasia. I was not sacrificing a living creature for experimentation. There had been a malfunction in the metamorphosis of the dragonfly. One wing had not fully developed. If left to live, the dragonfly soon would have become food for foraging ants.

For the previous week, scores of nymphs had been crawling out of the pond onto water plants and onto the bark of trees along the shore, and there, through the miracle of metamorphosis, they emerged as dragonflies.

I concentrated on one that crawled up and fastened its toes into the flower stalk of a blue iris. For nearly an hour it did not move. The stillness resembled death. Then it pushed its body away from the stalk, curving it upward in an arc. It repeated this movement several times, slowly at first, then more rapidly. Next it swung its body, in jerky movements, from side to side. If its curved toes had not been firmly embedded in the iris stalk, it would have fallen.

The nymph almost seemed to be resisting the change going on within it. But for this it was created. All the minnows, pollywogs, and members of its own species devoured during its period as a nymph were sacrificed to this end. If the nymph were to retain its form, the species would not survive. For in the nymphal state there is no mating, no reproducing of its kind, and only through the "veil of the shadow" of metamorphosis and the emergence of a dragonfly can the species be perpetuated.

The struggle, which in the nymph seemed so violent, is actually feeble when considered against the universal force directing the change. For there, in minutes, was being reenacted a pageant of change which had taken millenniums to perfect. And I had a ringside seat.

The struggle on the iris stalk continued. The body of the nymph grew longer, and the upward curves became more graceful. A crack began to open along the back, and widened quickly. First the head and eyes of the dragonfly emerged. They are the most amazing eyes in the realm of living creatures. Each has more than a thousand lenses, and each lens is connected by its own optic nerve to the central coordinating brain. With two such eyes the dragonfly is able to see objects in front of it, above and below, and quartering to the rear.

And they were developed in the dark regions of the pond. The intricate blueprint of their construction was contained in the egg the parent deposited in the pond last summer.

The thorax came out next, brilliant green, in contrast to the dull gray of the nymph. The head, including the eyes, and the thorax were larger than the section of the nymphal case out of which they came. Wings resembling crumpled cellophane emerged. Within their folds were veins and struts and the membranous cover to make up the functional wings of the dragonfly.

No wings were needed by the nymph. It traveled by "jet propulsion" through the water. The design of the wings anticipated use by the dragonfly for travel in the air.

The head and torso and the crumpled wings swung downward, and six legs were drawn, like swords, from the leg cases of the nymph. They were equipped with joints, tendons, nerves, veins, and muscles like those in the legs the nymph had used. But added to their sides were rows of short, stiff bristles to assist the dragonfly in capturing insects in a cage made by its legs when it is in flight.

The tip of the new body was still attached to the nymphal case. This supported it as it continued to hang down. For several minutes all body movement stopped, and once again it seemed dead. But through the transparent covering of its thorax, I could see the vital fluid pulsing, an indication that its heart was still beating.

Thirty minutes had elapsed since the crack first appeared. Then it began to flex its legs, and, suddenly, it sprang up and grasped the nymphal case with its toes, pulling the end of its body free.

In dreamlike slow motion the wings unfolded. The veins and struts within them hardened. The membrane became taut and turned a silvery sheen. At first the wings lay along the back and appeared to be two in number, but, as they dried, they sprang apart, and there were actually four. The curves of the thorax that supported them resembled those of a slim ballerina.

Abandoning the empty case, the dragonfly walked slowly up the iris stalk and stood transfigured on the blue flower, with wings that were bright and dazzling. A barely perceptible tremor passed through them, then increased and became a flutter. There was a soft rustling sound as they were revved up for flight. Then it sprang lightly into the air, and flew out across the pond. Still fastened to the iris flower stalk was the empty nymphal case out of which I had seen it emerge.

"And God said, Let the earth bring forth living creatures. And it was so. And God saw that it was good."

If I were destined by the wheel of life to return to the earth in the body of an insect, and if I had my choice, I'd choose that of a dragonfly, an *Anax junius* male, the kind I had watched emerging. And I'd not ask for shortcuts in the new life cycle. My new life would begin at the instant the spermatozoon of the male penetrated the covering of the female egg, causing fertilization. I'd incubate in the pond and hatch as a ferocious nymph, the scourge of minnows, fat pollywogs, and other aquatic creatures. I'd grow to maturity through many moltings, then on a sunny day, in some far distant June, I'd crawl out upon an iris stalk. There I would be initiated into the mystery of metamorphosis, discard my ugly nymphal casing, and with a glorified body rise up on silvery wings and mate in the air with a female of my own species.

The Great Blue Heron

The great blue heron is a serene bird, but his gaunt gray form in outline beside the pond is somewhat sinister. Standing there in waiting silence, he is sure death to frogs or fish coming within reach of his scythe-edged beak. His shadow fleeing over the ground when he is in flight is like an ill-omened spirit. A parasite, developed in his throat and passed out with the feces, brings death to fish and "swimmer's itch" to man. The heronry in which he breeds is redolent with the stench of death. His nests stand out as whited sepulchers in a graveyard of dead trees, killed by his lethal droppings. His young are fed on creatures smothered in the violence of his digestive juices. The throaty sounds he makes suggest the death rattle, and the clacking of his beak the knocking together of dry bones.

Early in June I visited a heronry on a small isolated lake not far from the pond. A game trail led from the water up through a grove of giant hemlock trees. Their heavy foliage blocked out the sun. The ground was covered with a dark carpet of decaying needles. A babel of unhappy sounds came through the woods as I neared the area where the nests were located, unearthly groans and guttural squawks containing no note of joy.

A rough-legged hawk, whose nest was in a hemlock tree, dove down at me, screeching his sharp staccato cry, "cheek, cheek,

cheek." He missed my head by inches. I felt the rush of air caused by his wings as he went by. His nest was near the heronry. He warned the birds of approaching danger and took heron fledglings for his watchman's fee.

Hearing his cry, the herons departed with a great thundering of wings. Their shadows cut through slanting beams of sunlight cast on the forest floor. None but the young remained when I reached the clearing where the nests were. I counted forty-eight nests. One tree held four. And all the trees with nests in them were dead, for all trees die that are "doomed to wear the nests of herons in their hair."

When herons mate, they bow and preen and strut like turkeycocks. They raise the ruff feathers on their heads and stroke each other's back and neck and lock their bills together, a gesture that in human courting would be described as kissing. Then after copulation, the male will offer the female a nest-building stick, as though in payment for her favors.

The ground was littered with the wrecks of nests that had fallen as limbs broke off and fell to the ground. For each spring herons build nests upon the foundations of the old ones, and after years of having sticks added to them, the nests get too heavy for a dead limb to bear. And herons have been nesting here for decades.

One of the nests had fallen recently and was intact. Curious to know how many sticks were in it, I began counting them. Some were the size of pencils; some nearly an inch in diameter. Each stick in the nest represented a flight from some distant point. I counted up to a thousand and gave up. There were at least a thousand more. Many heron-miles had been flown during the nest's construction.

Among the fallen nests were bones of fish, eggshells, and skeletons of young that had been pushed off the nest by stronger nestmates in their fight for food. Helpless on the ground, they starved to death or became the food of skunks or foxes or other predators,

for, unlike some birds, the great blue heron shows no parental concern for the stranded young.

Suddenly four in one of the nests stood up and craned their
necks, flapping their wings and making excited noises. Then high
up in the sky I saw an adult circling and begin spiraling down. It
was the parent from the nest in which the young were demonstrat-
ing. She was out of sight when they first became excited. Crouched
low in the nest, they could not have seen her, and I had heard no
sound from her, but by some uncanny sense they knew that she
was returning.

It was the female. She alighted on the far end of the limb, then
after assuring herself by turning her head and scanning the ground
below that no enemy was in sight, she walked gingerly along the
limb until she reached the nest. She used her outstretched wings for
balancing the way a high-wire walker uses his pole.

As I watched the herons and their clumsy movements on the
bare limbs above me and listened to the ugly sounds they made, I
had sympathy for them, doomed to live that kind of life. In fantasy
I created a special heaven to which all good heron spirits will go
after death. It will have shallow ponds well stocked with slow moving fish, and frogs with arthritis in their jumping legs. There will be
fields with many mice, and moles, and snakes, and turtles laying
eggs. The herons will build safe nests upon the ground. But the
most heavenly gift of all will be new vocal cords to produce sweet,
harmonious sounds. There will be no guttural squawks in my heron
heaven!

Within an hour all the birds had returned, and many of them
had taken off again for food. The pattern of behavior in the first
nest was repeated as each respective parent approached.

Newly hatched herons are fed in the same way as the young of
pigeons. The parents put their bills deep in the young one's throat
and give it partially digested food in semiliquid form. (For pigeons

this is referred to as "pigeon milk." Perhaps for herons it should be called "fish chowder.") As they get older, the semiliquid food injection ends. The parents then regurgitate their slimy loads of fish and frogs, crayfish and snakes, moles and meadow mice, and sometimes turtle eggs, directly into the nest. The young then scramble for the food, emitting noises suggesting hogs feeding at a swilling trough.

The young are "nest-broken" early, and splatter their excrement over the edges of the nest. This is the stuff that kills the trees.

Man through the ages has been puzzled by the different forms in which life appears on earth. While functionally alike, with similar basic organs, the forms are vastly different. Evolution, natural selection, survival of the fittest, and mutations caused when random particles from outer space collide with the heredity genes are some of the explanations for the diversity. Yet despite these theories there does not seem to have been time enough since life appeared to account for the difference between a heron and a hummingbird, a man and a mouse. Perhaps in the beginning mutations were more frequent.

There was a great blue heron male that often visited the pond. He usually arrived an hour before sunset and landed near the cattails, where the water from the spring flowed into the pond. He'd fish there until his form became enveloped in the shadows of the approaching night. Then he'd fly off, his long neck folded in flying stance, his legs stretched out behind him, feet together, toes pointed, and rise high above the trees with his wings beating a slow and silent rhythm, flying into the sunset. I often watched him while the magic spell of distance intervened to change him from a flying bird with wings six feet across to a mere speck against the western sky.

It seemed as though another day, with work complete, had also left the pond, to follow the illuminated path left by the setting sun.

Mornings, before the sun was up, I'd often see a great blue

heron standing among the stark white trees in the marsh below the old beaver dam. I sometimes wondered if he was the same that I had watched going west the night before, if he, somehow, had overtaken the sun in the earth tunnel, where it had paused to change the days, and had managed to fly on ahead and wait in the marsh for the new day.

Late in August I made another trip to the heronry among the hemlocks. While still a hundred yards away, I stopped and listened. No raucous sounds greeted me. No rough-legged hawk dove down. No somber shadows of flying birds interrupted the spots of sunlight on the forest floor. Their nesting project accomplished, the birds had all gone south to spend the winter there.

There were many fallen nests and bones of young beneath the whitened trees. On one leg bone there were fine grooves that gnawing teeth of mice had made as they fed on the mineral content. These minerals had been transformed from the bones of fish to the bones of the heron, and would become an element in the bones of mice as well. When the mice died, the minerals would be passed to smaller creatures and finally be returned as basic and indestructible elements to earth. Life would have made use of them in many forms before they were discarded.

Tremendous energy had been expended by these great blue herons in carrying out the plan of life. Miles had been flown, nests built, and countless hours spent beside ponds and streams collecting food. All of this was to preserve the species so that it would not perish from the earth. Even the empty nests silhouetted against the sky were symbols of this life cycle. The nests will remain there through rains, snow, and ice, until the birds return next spring to set the cycle in motion again.

Lords of the Cattails

The redwing blackbirds owned the cattail area of the pond by "squatters' rights." When I moved into the cabin, the males had already staked out their territorial claims and were busy selecting the females who would share the "homesites" with them.

The males had come north two weeks before, and each had fought to establish his rights to the area he selected. Most of the fighting had been done by tone of voice and posture. They made threatening gestures and displayed the brilliant wing epaulets that, in the redwing, are the badge of maleness. There was some chasing and physical contact, but bluffing played the biggest part. Vocal sounds are important in the pecking order of many birds.

It seemed quite obvious that redwing males are conscious of their brilliant epaulets and know that they attract attention. When a hawk flies over the territory or perches in a nearby tree, the males sit still and keep their colored feathers out of sight. When a male is trespassing an another's territory and doesn't want to be conspicuous, he also hides the color.

The cattail area of the pond had been divided among three males. So definite was the division that a map outlining each plot could have been drawn on paper. In many cases the boundary line ran between cattails only feet apart. Any trespassing called for quick action. There must have been a mental map inscribed in each bird's brain, for each respected the others' territories.

Two things made for the ideal nesting site. One was dense cattails in which the nest could be hidden from flying predators, the hawks, the crows, the blue jays. The second was a high vantage point, a perch in a pondside tree, from which the male could survey his territory and dive down upon intruders. Here, too, he could give vent to his call of "okalee" while displaying his gaudy feather patches.

After the territories had been established and while waiting for the females to arrive, the males spent time posturing and chasing off transient "claim jumpers."

The females arrived singly and in small groups. They flew about the pond investigating different nesting sites. They perched in trees and flipped their tails and gave short, tantalizing female calls, "cheek-cheek-cheek."

A male would fly up to the branch on which the female sat and hop along it toward her. He'd spread his wings and show his colors and fly down among the cattails in his territory and give his song-spread there, like a salesman calling attention to the good points in a piece of real estate. If the female showed no interest and flew away, the male would follow and try to lure her back. He would be joined by other males, and there would be a chase.

Sometimes a female would dive suddenly into a clump of cattails and remain there for several minutes. The male whose territory it was would fly in after her and strut with wings extended to indicate that she was exciting him. Meanwhile, the male in the adjacent territory would come up to the border and try to coax the female to come and see what he had to offer. If he trespassed the boundary line, he would be driven off with vicious peckings.

For many days the air about the pond was filled with the excitement of mate-choosing. Then, as the birds paired off, the excitement died down, and the serious business of perpetuating the red-wing heritage began.

A female usually visited several territories before she made her choice. In choosing the site in which to build her nest, she also accepted the owner of it as her mate. He automatically went with the property. As I watched them going about the business of choosing a nesting site, it was clear that location was important and that any male would do. But once the female had made her choice and indicated it by remaining in the cattails for some time, the male assumed complete domination. If other males approached her, he drove them off. If she visited other sites, perhaps to change her mind, he would go after her and drive her back. When she left the pond on feeding flights, he followed along.

The male whose territory was nearest the cabin was the first to get a mate. I had the feeling that this had been his territory the year before, and that the female who chose to share it with him was his former mate. But he was still obliged to do some fighting to re-establish his claim, both to the territory and to her. But it was evident from the size and brilliance of his wing patches that he was the dominant male of the three.

A map of the area that the male controlled must also have been imprinted in the female's brain. Her actions indicated that she, too, knew its boundaries. If another female trespassed on it, she drove her off. If she was pursued by other males, she flew back to the home territory and gave the alarm call to her mate.

The courtship of the redwings follows a set pattern that ultimately leads to the act of mating. There is much chasing of the female, much posturing, and many mating sounds. The final act is quite dramatic. Here it is described by Robert Nero, who spent three years studying redwing behavior in a Wisconsin marsh:

"The female gives a long rapid series of soft whimpering notes. In low intensity, the call is slow, two sounds: 'tse-sit,' or 'seek-

seek.' But later the speed of the delivery increases and these become: 'tsee-tsee-tsee.' These calls are sometimes given while she
is perched in a high tree, but usually on, or near, the ground. As the
intensity of the display increases, she leans forward, lifts her tail
and wings, sometimes raising her head slightly and whimpering.

"The male reacts to the female display by perching close to
her in the crouch position. If her display is limited to whimpering
and wing flutter, he may do nothing more and pay little attention
to her. But when she goes into full display, he shows excitement.
He flutters his wing tips while holding them out, either raised or
lowered, and gives a soft whimpering cry similar to the female's.
But not as loud, and usually not as long. Then with head erect, and
violently shaking epaulets, puffed-out feathers, lowered and spread
tail, and lowered head, he silently walks stiffly to the displaying
female.

"He sometimes walks for several feet, awkwardly climbing
over obstructions. On one occasion a male walked five feet along
the ground toward a displaying female and then, still fluttering his
wings, flew over an intervening cattail clump and landed directly
on top of the female, who had been out of his sight.

"After dismounting, the male moves off without further conspicuous display. And during copulation the female is silent and
almost motionless. But afterward she may give the call, flutter her
wings, and preen. On one occasion after the male had left the female, she went into the precopulatory display again, giving an
even louder and more rapid whimpering call than she had previ-
ously given."

As soon as the pairing bond had been established, the male
began to show concern about getting the nest built. Only the female does the constructing. The male flies into a dense part of the
cattails and performs nest-building motions. He picks up bits of

cattail stems and takes them to the site and makes scolding sounds as though urging the female to get to work.

Three weeks after the pair nearest the cabin had mated, the nest was completed and the first egg laid. Once again the male began to show anxiety. He perched on the edge of the nest, looked at the single egg, and scolded the female. It is doubtful that redwings can count, but there must have been a pattern of more than one egg in a nest established in his brain. After the third one was laid, he settled down and was again relaxed. Only when she was away on feeding flights, or off the eggs longer than he thought necessary, did he again show concern.

The daily rhythm in animal feeding known as the solunar period was quite obvious at the pond. For some time all would be comparatively still. Then, as though a signal had been given, there would be a sudden surge of life. Sometimes the redwings left the pond area on feeding flights to fields and to the edges of the highway to collect small stones for grinding the food in their gizzards. But always during these feeding breaks, there would be an armistice to fighting. Birds that were rivals on the pond ate side by side as friends.

In many species of birds the males bring food to the nesting females. Not so with redwings. The male sits upon his perch, posturing and giving his calls, while the female gets her own food.

Often I sat among the cattails and watched the female in the nest nearest the cabin feeding her young. The male does not help her with this chore, either.

One morning after the young had feathered and were nearly ready for flight, I found the male agitatedly flying about in circles above the nest. I waited for the female to return with food, and when she didn't, I went closer to the nest. There were only two young ones in it. There had been three the day before. Thinking one had fallen out, I searched among the cattails but found no trace. Then I went back to dry land and watched through the binoculars. The female did not return. Instead the male came in with insects in his beak and, standing on the edge of the nest, fed the young. I'd never known of redwing males doing this. Later in the day I checked again, and he was still feeding them. I realized that something had happened to her. Either she had been run over by an automobile while collecting gravel on the highway, or she had been killed defending the nest when the young one had been taken.

The nest was well hidden and could not be seen by predators from above. The clump of cattails in which it had been built was in the water. I doubted that a weasel would have ventured out that far. Perhaps a mink had been responsible. But he would have left tracks in the mud. More than likely it had been a snake that had done the killing.

For several days the male continued feeding the young. At my approach, he'd circle low and make threatening sounds. Then one morning he sat upon his perch without attacking. The nest was empty. At first I thought the remaining two had started flying. But if they had, they would have been somewhere near, and the male would have been guarding them. I was now certain that the snake had returned.

The behavior of the redwings about the pond and marsh changed after their young left the nests. They became sociable again and went about in groups, without fighting. There was now no further need for competition; no females to protect; no private property bounds to defend. The world and what was in it belonged to them all.

By late August, the pond was free of redwings. I thought they had all gone south. But early in September I came across them— this time in a wild rice marsh on the banks of the Wisconsin River near Rhinelander. They were in one great flock that numbered thousands. They were fattening up on the rice before starting for the long trip south.

The man who owned the marsh did not appreciate them. Ten thousand birds can eat many pounds of rice in a day, and wild rice was then selling for two dollars a pound!

Swallows

If swallows spoke the languages of the countries they had traveled over to reach the pond, the air would be filled with a babel of bird tongues. Portuguese and Spanish would predominate. But there would also be smatterings of Haitian-French, Mayan, and Zapotec, and their English would have a Scandinavian accent picked up from the Wisconsin farmers.

The pond would be quite different without the swallows. The swooping, darting, curving paths they make from dawn to dusk while collecting food become as natural to the scenery as the cattails, water lilies, and muskrat houses.

Insects triggered to emerge at different periods throughout the spring and summer months provide a variety of "blue-plate" swallow food served on the wing.

Swallows make accurate barometers, too. When they fly low across the water, with wing tips almost touching, bad weather is in store. When they fly high, the weather will be clearing. The altitude of the flight of insects upon which they feed is determined by the atmospheric pressure.

The feeding patterns of swallows are very much alike. All food is taken on the wing. But in the ways they build their nests, there are differences. The purple martins are the aristocrats of the swallow world. Those visiting the pond laid their eggs and raised their young in a three-story house fastened to the frame of a windmill on a nearby farm. When they arrived in the spring, they found the house clean, with a wall-to-wall carpet of fresh straw. Like the farmhouse, in which the human beings live, the swallow house was painted white and had a shingled roof.

They paid their rent by being decorative and keeping the farmyard free of insects. Purple martins returning to the same farm every year are considered a good omen. They bring the farmer luck.

The barn swallows, the only members of the swallow world to have a true forked swallowtail, also nested on the same farm. But they were not as pampered as the martins. They were obliged to build their own nests of mud and straw in the shelter of the cow shed.

A great blue heron showed me where the tree swallows nested. One morning, just at daybreak, I was watching him "frogging" in the marsh near a dead poplar tree. Two birds began attacking him. As each one dove, the heron crouched and made a futile attempt to defend himself with his beak. But the birds were much too agile for his clumsy movements, and he gave up the fight and flew away.

From the cabin, through binoculars, the attackers seemed as small as bees. But the pure white breasts and steel-blue backs identified them as tree swallows. Their nest was in a hole high up in the dead poplar tree. And there were young ones in it. When I walked to where the heron had stood, they promptly dove at me. With the arrival of parenthood in many animals comes a new-found courage, and threatening objects, whether heron or man, will be attacked.

I moved to another tree some yards away and leaned against it while I watched them. They went about their business of catching insects but were still suspicious of my presence. Before they entered their nest with food for the young ones, they perched upon a limb above and looked at me. They looked first with one eye,

then, as though not trusting it, cocked their heads and looked at me with the other one.

I saw the female come in with a large crane fly held by a hind leg. She had evidently captured it from behind. While she was watching me, the leg came off and the crane fly flew away. She sprang out and brought it back, this time held firmly by its middle.

The hole in the tree in which the swallows were nesting had been dug by a woodpecker. The swallow bill is not designed for such demanding work. It can be used for building nests with mud, and, opened wide, it can capture insects as the bird flies through swarms of them. And that is enough.

Another species at the pond were the cliff swallows. I located their nests on the side of a barn some miles from the pond. They build a gourd-shaped nest with a long neck curving downward to keep out the weather. The opening is just large enough for the birds to squeeze in. Both males and females carry mud, and both work at nest-building.

Above a stream that curves through a pasture on another farm, the bank swallows do their nesting in deep tunnels. The colony has returned to this same spot for many generations of both farmers and birds. Each spring when they arrive, they clean out and deepen the tunnels of the previous year.

At first I rated the bank swallows far down on the swallow totem pole. But after spending time in the pasture observing them, I changed my estimate. Now I rank them near the top. They do not inhabit gaudy houses provided by man, nor pay rent by entertaining people and bringing luck. They do not appropriate the nests dug in dead trees by other birds. Nor do they raise their young in steamy barns above the cows. Their nests are never washed away by sudden storms the way those of the cliff swallows are. Instead they have the whole earth for the sides and floors and roofs. And they live beside a running stream that brings much of their food flying past their doors.

One of the most peculiar patterns of behavior in the insect world occurs inside the tunnels of the bank swallows. There a parasitic flea lives. It does not feed upon swallow blood, but depends for nourishment on the bits of refuse on the feathers the birds discard. When the swallows leave at the end of the breeding season, and there is no further food for the fleas, they change into pupae, which require no new food, and remain in the tunnels until the birds return in the spring. They then emerge as fleas once again, and the life cycle is renewed.

The emerging mechanism of most pupae is controlled by growth light, or temperature, or a combination of all three. But in the deep tunnels of the swallows there is always darkness and very little change in temperature. The factor that triggers the emerging mechanism of the pupae is the presence of the swallows as they begin their annual nesting activities again.

Baffling indeed are the methods used by life to perpetuate the different forms it takes.

Reactions

One quiet evening in late June the sun set, and with it the noises of the day departed. Those of the night were about to begin. The surface of the pond was broken by the lazy circlings of whirligigs or by the dimple a minnow made when it reached up for food.

A neighbor farmer came to visit, and we were sitting on the bank of the pond, near the old beaver dam. He had been suspicious of me when I first arrived. A city man wandering about at all hours of the day and night, carrying binoculars and a notebook, and not working, not even fishing. Then, as time passed, his suspicions ended. He began to walk over after his evening chores and drink a can of beer and visit. We talked of many things, especially those having to do with nature. Living on a farm in the country all of his life, he had accumulated a great fund of natural knowledge.

We began talking about the way a school of fish react when a stone is suddenly dropped among them. I'd taken it for granted that they all saw the stone approaching and dashed away from it. But as I thought more about it, I realized that the fish on the outside of the school could not see the falling stone, and the scattering took place in large, as well as small, schools. It was not a chain reaction passed on by those nearest the stone to the others. There had to be some other explanation; the movement in all the fish was instantaneous.

I asked the farmer if he knew the answer. He hesitated, thinking that I was joshing him, a city man being smart. But when he realized I was serious, he said simply, "Waves."

He then stood up and stamped his foot violently on the ground at the water's edge. Instantly hundreds of tiny circles appeared upon the surface. He waited until they had all dispersed, then stamped his foot again. The circles began as mysteriously as before. Those far out appeared at the same time as the ones nearer the shore. An observer on the opposite shore would have seen them before hearing the sound made by the stamping foot. They were like the circles made by the first drops of a shower of rain.

The farmer said they were caused by those minnows swimming near the surface that were stimulated by the sound waves generated when his foot hit the ground. The sound traveled through the water more rapidly than the sound waves moved through the air.

He had always used this stamping method for locating schools of minnows he seined for bait. He was surprised that I had never heard of it.

Often when the pond was still, I walked along the bank and stamped my foot to see the circles appear. But it wasn't reasonable to me that such feeble waves, traveling through the water, could penetrate the scale covering of fish and cause the sudden reaction. This minor problem did not disturb the farmer. He knew the waves generated were responsible, he cared not how they operated.

Months later a professor of ichthyology at Southern Illinois University explained the process. He took a pickled fish out of a jar of brine, wiped off the moisture, and placed the fish under a low-powered microscope. Along each side I could see a row of holes that penetrated the scales and skin. When the fish was living, water filled the holes, and sensitive nerve endings were suspended in each one. The slightest vibration in the water stimulated the nerves on the side of the fish from which the vibrations originated. And the fish would react as a man does when the dentist's drill touches an exposed nerve—by attempting to move away.

It is sad indeed that hidden in museum vaults, in books and pamphlets, written in language that only the initiated can understand, or in the memories of such men as the farmer, a vast fund of information reposes about the basic facts of life, and few human beings know anything about them.

The Cecropia Moth

Soon after I moved into the cabin, and before the leaves were out on the trees, I found the large cocoon of a Cecropia moth fastened to a branch on a willow down near the pond. I cut off the branch and hung it in a wire cage to wait for the emerging.

Late the previous year, the cocoon had been spun by a green caterpillar. Early that year, the caterpillar had hatched from an egg laid by a moth. It had spent the summer feeding upon the willow leaves. As it grew, its skin grew tight, the old skin was shed, and a new one replaced it. This molting procedure had happened nine times, and the caterpillar had grown to over four inches in length. Then, late in August, controlling growth hormones located behind the brain had called a halt to feeding; the caterpillar had crawled out on the branch and spun the cocoon.

While it had been feeding, a clear, viscous fluid was being stored in two thick-walled sacs along the body. This fluid, secreted from glands near the mouth, formed a silken thread for building the cocoon. There was enough fluid to spin over six hundred yards of cocoon silk.

Spinning is often associated with spiders but not with caterpillars. This particular one raises the forepart of its body and slowly moved its head from side to side in a figure eight. The first few strands of silk paid out are fastened to nearby twigs and leaves, the strands far apart. Then, as other strands are added, they overlap upon each other, until the caterpillar is completely encased in closely woven fabric. When dry, it resembles parchment and is impervious to both moisture and cold. The thread the caterpillar spun is hollow, and the air space provides good insulation. Nylon thread spun by machines is solid, and women have discovered that stockings woven from nylon are cold. Real silk also contains a hollow core, and stockings made from silk retain body warmth.

One morning, late in June, the end of the cocoon became moist. This indicated that the moth was about to emerge. It had exuded a drop of acid which softened the tough fabric, making it possible to push its way through the cocoon. As I watched, the fabric split and a head containing two antennae appeared. The antennae were narrow, those of a female. The male antennae are wide and feathery. The body quickly followed, covered with fine flakes of a fabric that resembled fur. The flakes were of many colors, with red predominant. The wings, crumpled by the confinement in the cocoon, slowly unfolded until they were over four inches across. And upon them, produced by row upon row of the colored flakes, was the unmistakable wing pattern of the Cecropia.

Students sitting in a football stadium, suddenly spelling out the name of their school by displaying sheets of lettered cardboard, have to plan carefully what appears so spontaneous. Each cardholder has to sit in the proper place if success is to be achieved. I wondered how, during the months when the wings were being formed in the cocoon on the willow branch, the thousands of colored flakes had been arranged to "spell out" the Cecropia pattern.

Another mystery that intrigued me had also taken place in the blacked-out secrecy of the cocoon: How had all the brilliant colors been produced from masticated willow leaves?

The moth spent the afternoon hanging, motionless. To all appearances she was resting. But had I been equipped with the chemo-receptors of the male Cecropia moth, I would have detected the scented invitations she was busily sending out.

Until recently it was not thought possible that a pheromone sent out to advertise the female's presence could be powerful enough to be effective for any practical distance. The French naturalist Jean Henri Fabre felt that she must have another form of communication, perhaps air waves produced by her antennae. He said one might just as well expect to tint an entire lake with a single drop of carmine. His analogy was correct, for to the male moth's powerful chemoreceptors a "lake," a mile or more in extent, is effectively "tinted" with a very small amount of the pheromone exuded by the female.

The first male caller arrived just after sunset. He circled above the cage, then landed on it. By eight o'clock, six other males had arrived. I captured the largest of the suitors and put him in the cage, where he quickly mated with the female. She stopped sending out the "invitation," the other males soon left, and no others came.

After photographing them, I put the mated pair in an empty shoe box for the night. By next morning they had separated, and over a hundred eggs had been deposited in patches on the sides and cover of the box. I released the male, and he flew away to answer other possible invitations.

Days later I photographed the tiny caterpillars crawling out of the eggs. I put them on the willow tree, and they began feeding upon the leaves. It was difficult for me to comprehend the potentialities contained within each crawling creature. The majority would become food for birds, but many would grow, and molt, and before the coming of frost wrap themselves in silken thread and begin again the long period of metamorphosis that would change them into moths. None of these caterpillars would have been here had not the male picked up the female's scented information and, through the act of mating, transferred his sperm to vitalize the eggs.

The female lived for another day, then died. Moths of this species have no facilities for eating. They emerge, they attract a male, they mate, they lay their eggs, they die. She was loaded with eggs, and would have laid them even though she had not mated. But they would not have hatched.

To me, the beautiful designs on the Cecropia's wings seemed wasted. For, unlike some birds, whose gaudy plumage is a visible sex attractant, the moth depends upon scent alone. The female of the human species depends upon both.

A July Afternoon

One muggy July afternoon, when the barometer was low and thunderclouds threatened, life seemed still. Following the path from the cabin, I entered the dark coolness of the woods. As I walked, I left behind me in the humid air a scented trail made by the blood that was coursing through my veins. Scores of mosquitoes picked it up, and when I paused, they swarmed about me. Pregnant females in need of blood to nourish their eggs, they were after me, that blood supply.

They circled me in a frenzied dance, making a high-pitched sound with their beating wings that was almost barbaric. It was a universal sound that hunting creatures make when stimulated by the smell of blood.

One settled on the back of my hand and, stalking through the hairy forest, probed for an opening in the skin in which to insert her beak. No need had she for a willow wand. The odor of blood flowing close to the surface rose about her like miasma from a fetid swamp.

She found a pore, inserted her beak, touched a nerve, and the "dew-line" of my vast nervous system sent pain warnings to my brain. My involuntary impulse was to kill her. As a superior member of the animal world, I held over this lesser creature the power of death. But she intrigued me, and I decided to let her live. I possess a boundless supply of blood compared to her small needs.

Though lower in the scale of life, she had capabilities I do not have. She had the ability to pick up the faint trail that I left and follow it to the source. The proboscis through which she drew blood is not only a needle for piercing skin but also a tube through which to siphon blood. Also, it is a device through which she injects a fluid to prevent the blood from clotting.

Her abdomen filled quickly and became a taut balloon. As she started to pull away I carefully stretched the skin around the pore and held her fast. Blood-getting had been far too easy for her. Feeling the pressure she braced her feet and set her wings in motion, but the vise held and she was my captive.

Then I relented and released the skin, and she took off in flight toward the pond. Her load was heavy and her flight was downward. Finally she landed at the edge of a pool of stagnant water, yards short of her objective. But there was sufficient water for her needs.

There she would lay her eggs, and, nourished by the blood I gave her, they would hatch and, after the larval and pupal stages in the water, arise as creatures capable of sending out calls for mates with wing vibrations, and of searching for blood, perhaps again from me.

Strange, in the mysterious chain of life in which we are all involved, that blood from me, a human being, can be utilized by mosquitoes. I smiled and thought of Kipling's "The Captain's lady and Suzy O'Grady are sisters under the skin." I wondered whether the type of blood was important to mosquitoes. Mine is type B.

Leaving the coolness of the woods, I stepped out again upon the path. Mosquitoes did not follow me. The thunderclouds had drifted off. The sun was bright in an untroubled sky. I sat upon the bank of the pond, my back against the trunk of a willow tree. The odor of my perspiration began attracting carrion flies. They do not sting but feed upon the body wastes contained in the perspiration. I crushed a fly and threw the quivering body among a group of whirligig beetles collected in the shelter of a curved willow root below me. They scattered at the impact. Then one returned and grabbed the fly. He moved off in a zigzag course across the glassy surface, pushing the fly in front of him, like a hockey player with a puck. Two others chased him. For several moments he "outskated" them. But eventually they caught up with him, and all three attached their beaks as they whirled in a tight circle, sucking out the juices from the fly. The empty carcass was left to become food for snails and other lower forms of life. No particle of the fly would be wasted.

The seeming stillness of the pond was quite deceptive. Below the calm surface was a never ending cycle of life and death, a continuing struggle for existence. There, minute forms of life fed upon the algae. Crustaceans and small fish ate these. Large fish devoured the smaller ones, and snapping turtles ate both large and small.

Within the pond were uncounted eggs, in sacs and clusters, clinging to the stems and leaves of plants or floating freely through the water. "One wondrous mass awaiting the vital breath, when heaven shall bid the spirit blow."

Above the pond the air was filled with darting dragonflies. Myriad silver wings reflected the radiance of the sun. Two *Anax junius* males patrolled the air directly overhead. A female joined them and they both attempted to capture her for mating. True to the universal behavior of the female when pursued by males, she attempted to evade them.

I was treated to a spectacular show of aerobatics as these, the greatest fliers in the insect world, moved into action. They swooped, and hovered, and darted straight ahead, and dived, weaving in and out in intricate maneuvers at speeds sometimes too fast for me to follow.

One of the males outwitted a female on a turn and quickly grasped her behind the head with a pair of claspers on the end of his body designed for this sole purpose. The pair then flew about in tandem; the male above, the female below, their wings in perfect synchronization, like an airplane being refueled in flight.

The female then curved her slim body downward and forward, and with the tip located the penis of the male near the base of his wings. Two protruding hamuli engaged her genitals and held them fast while she collected the sperm.

The female can attach her genitals to her species, and hers alone. The genital segments of an *Anax junius* female will not mesh with the male hamuli of another species. Like a Yale lock, the hamuli of the male are grooved and only a "key" with matching grooves will fit.

It took several minutes to transfer the sperm, and then the body of the female was once again straightened out, behind that of the male. Still firmly clasped together, they alighted on a partly submerged log. Walking slowly backward to the water, the female pushed the tip of her body below the surface, and "feeling" along the bark, until she found a crack, she deposited her many eggs. The purpose of their mating then had been fulfilled, and they separated and flew away.

After such a dramatic mating ceremony, it would seem appropriate for the eggs to hatch out into little dragonflies, the way bird eggs hatch into little birds. Then the parents and the young could fly away together in a V-formation toward the south. But such is not the plan of life for dragonflies. It is many months and many stages of existence later that the young dragonflies emerge, their parents long since dead.

A series of small ripples rose upon the water's surface, just above the point where the dragonfly deposited her eggs. A minnow began feeding upon the eggs not hidden in the crack. Eggs of the dragonfly were being sacrificed to perpetuate the heritage of minnows.

There is an amusing quirk of fate inherent in this pattern. It is entirely possible that a dragonfly nymph, hatched from one of the eggs the minnow did not find, could, when fully grown the following spring, capture and devour the same minnow; for minnows are the favorite food of nymphs.

Thoughts on Spiders

In mid-August I was sitting among the cattails watching a muskrat feeding in a bed of pondweed. Quite by accident I became aware of spider activity in the cattails, and my interest in the muskrat waned.

Capturing a newly hatched spider, I confined her on the back of my hand with the rim of the magnifying glass. She made frantic efforts to escape, then, finding no way out, relaxed and began spinning a web among the hairs of my hand. How wonderful it would be if human beings could so readily adapt when they suddenly find themselves confined.

I put her back on the cattail where web-spinning would be rewarded, and watched her as she started to spin another web.

How had this mite of spider life survived to spin this web among the cattails? And how had she acquired her web-spinning ability? The information she used had been imprinted on an inherited "tape" within her microscopic brain, a tape, perfected by her ancestors through countless generations of trial and error in web-spinning technique, available at her need to be "played back" to her. And she in turn would pass it on to her descendants.

As I watched her begin the web, it occurred to me that there must be some other source of information upon which she could rely. For there among the cattails was a unique construction problem. She had to select the anchor points to which the guy lines of her web were to be fastened. Such understanding could not have been anticipated and recorded on the tape. Only when the guy lines had been established could the tape take over and let her spin an orb identical to those spun by other spiders.

This particular spider had had no visible nourishment since she had come out of the egg. She already possessed the substance in her body out of which the web was made, and with it came the intricate mechanism for turning that substance into a single thread of several strands. As she paid out the thread, she fastened each junction at the point at which it crossed one of the spoke threads with a drop of glue.

A second newly hatched spider swung down on a silken thread and walked across the eyepiece of my binoculars. If she could have adjusted her spider vision to the matched lenses in that human instrument, she, like man, could have seen far beyond her cattail world.

While I was watching the latest visitor, the first spider had industriously worked on her web. Before it was completed she caught a mosquito in it. Quickly she stopped the beating of the wings with strands of silk. Then, injecting a digestive enzyme that liquefied the tissues in the mosquito, she sucked the insect dry. This was her first meal on earth. In my reactions as a human being I hoped she'd capture many more, live long enough to mate and lay her eggs, and, through them, pass on her spider heritage to other generations.

But that first web might well be her last. Before the day ended there was the risk of being captured and imprisoned in the cell of a mud-dauber wasp. Her body, with its complicated genes of spider inheritance, could easily be sacrificed as food to perpetuate the life-stream of a wasp.

As the sun got higher and the day got hotter, I left the cattails

to lie on my back among the weeds in the abandoned field, to rest and listen to nature's sounds. A jumping spider hopped across my face, and I sat up. I tried to catch her, but she was much too agile. That species makes no web. She stalks her prey and springs upon it. She is a proper huntress.

Another spider on a tall sheaf of grass was busy web-building, too. One end of the web was attached to a spear of grass three feet away. She hastily crawled out on this single strand, not upright like a circus aerialist, but clinging to it with her body hanging upside down. Halfway across she suddenly let go and landed upon a blade of grass just inches from the ground. A strand of web was paid out from her spinnerets as she fell. She secured it to the blade of grass and climbed back up to the long supporting thread. Her movements were very rapid as, moving from point to point and over the space across which she intended to construct her web, she anchored guy lines and added cross supports.

Like the spider in the cattails, she had never seen this spot before. Being nearsighted, as all spiders are, she could not have scanned it from the spear of grass before she started her web. The first strand of the web was fastened to the spear of grass by chance. She had paid it out, and it had floated on the light breeze and attached itself. But all the actions after that appeared to be according to a plan.

Like this spider, we, too, send out strands of thought. If, by chance, they make contact with some unseen object in the vast unknown, we, too, can use them as anchor lines for building webs beyond the spear of grass on which we stand.

I lay back in the weeds again and looked straight up. Bright clouds were drifting through an azure sky. A tiny, silvery thing sailed overhead. I captured it and discovered a spider of another type attached to a web. It had not stood on a spear of grass paying out its web and waiting for it to make contact with some distant object. Instead, it sailed out on the web with seeming faith that it would find something on which it could anchor.

As the breeze grew stronger, many of these small spiders could be found sailing into space with their single threads trailing them. The air was crisscrossed with these shining monorails.

Pulling my cap across my eyes, I fell asleep. When I awoke, the air was free of spiders. As I rose to my feet, dozens of them were carried up with me. Their silken cords attaching my body to the earth were broken. I carefully brushed them off and wondered what had happened to the little jumping spider. No doubt she was stalking food, while these others were setting their traps and waiting for their food to come to them. In the process of anchoring their many guy lines to the weeds and grasses, they had bound the sleeping Gulliver to the abandoned field, even though their food-getting efforts had not been successful.

> A noiseless patient spider,
> I mark'd where on a little promontory it stood isolated,
> Mark'd how to explore the vacant vast surrounding,
> It launch'd forth filament, filament, filament, out of itself,
> Ever unreeling them, ever tirelessly speeding them.
>
> And you O my soul where you stand,
> Surrounded, detached, in measureless oceans of space,
> Ceaselessly musing, venturing, throwing,
>   seeking the spheres to connect them,
> Till the bridge you will need be form'd,
>   till the ductile anchor hold,
> Till the gossamer thread you fling
>   catch somewhere, O my soul.
>
> —WALT WHITMAN

Mosquitoes

The first mosquito of the night sounded the call to arms—to arms, to legs, to face, to neck, to any part of the anatomy that was exposed. The call was picked up by a host of others, and they all rallied to it. On swiftly moving wings, each mosquito brought an empty stomach. Connected to each was a hypodermic needle, sharpened to pierce my skin, and if I remained outside, countless mosquito stomachs would be filled with my blood.

With memories of past night assaults, I waved my handkerchief, in token of a white flag of surrender, and sadly went indoors.

The strange biological need for blood in the life cycle of this tiny member of the fly family has been the most important single factor in altering the face of human history. Because of it, civilizations have been destroyed, empires overthrown, cities abandoned, wars lost, and countless millions of human beings slain.

Anopheles, the mosquito that sits with its tail high in the air, by spreading malarial parasites has been the greatest killer in human history. But though often suspected of the crime, she was not officially proven guilty until August 20, 1897, Mosquito Day.

It was John Ross, a surgeon in the British Indian army, who supplied the evidence to convict her, and he came close to failure. Though he had identified the malarial parasite in the blood of a man who had the fever, when he transferred this blood, the way he thought the mosquito did, into the veins of another man who did not have the fever, there was no carry-over. The mystery became more baffling when, after a mosquito had filled its stomach with infected blood, and the blood in the mosquito was examined under a microscope, it was seen that the shape of the parasites had changed from those seen in the bloodstream of the man. Ross saw two different shapes, one crescent-shaped, the other with a tail. While he watched, those with the tail disappeared and, shortly afterward, the others vanished.

This indicated that the parasites with tails were males and that they had entered the crescent-shaped females, to fertilize them. The females could only have disappeared by traveling to some other part of the mosquito.

After much microscopic detective-searching, Ross located the females in the saliva glands. From there they would be injected into the human bloodstream, where they would multiply asexually in the red corpuscles.

The onset of fever would complete the circle. But without the mosquito as the middle agent, the parasites could not conjugate and complete the life cycle.

I had no fear of getting malaria from the mosquitoes around the pond. They were of the harmless *Culex* genus, though their stings were just as painful as those of the *Anopheles.* In any case, the mosquitoes would have to have malaria, be sick mosquitoes, before being able to pass it on.

The power of survival in the mosquito family is amazing. They all need water in the early larval stage of their development, but very little water will suffice. Any receptacle that will hold water for ten days will serve their breeding purpose: a tiny stagnant pool, an empty tin can, a coconut shell. I was with the troops during the Villa trouble on the Mexican border. When we were plagued with attacks of dengue fever, also spread by mosquitoes, Dr. Gay, from Rush Medical School, serving with the First Illinois Cavalry, counted over five thousand mosquito "wigglers" in the hoofprints of a horse that had been made in the Texas gumbo and filled with rainwater.

Mosquitoes can pass the winter as eggs or larvae or can hibernate as adults. One species, *Wyeoma smithii*, which breeds in pitcher plants in swamps, can remain frozen in the ice all winter and renew its activities with the first thaw of spring.

On a dogsled trip through the wilds of western Canada some years ago, we cut down a large dead Norway pine for the night's fuel. The bark came loose when the tree fell, and between it and the trunk were countless thousands of mosquitoes, massed in winter hibernation.

Mosquitoes multiply rapidly. Some species can produce a new generation in two weeks. The eggs hatch in forty-eight hours; the larvae mature in seven days; the final pupal stage lasts for two. Two days after a female emerges, she can broadcast signals for a mate, locate blood for nourishing her eggs, and lay as many as three hundred.

A disquieting thought intruded into the world of this conflict with respect to what we label "good" and what we term "evil." The mosquito causes pain when she collects blood to satisfy her need to fertilize her eggs. We label this evil. But for the mosquito this is good. Unlike wasps and bees and centipedes and scorpions, the mosquito does not sting in anger. In addition, not all mosquitoes that draw blood do spread disease. To the parasite that uses the mosquito to complete its life cycle, the mosquito is a beneficiary, a thing that's good. To the sporozoites developing in the red corpuscles of the malaria victim, the shaking with fever is a sign of health and therefore is good; to the victim of the fever, it is bad.

From the beginning of time, the mosquito has played its role, and until Mosquito Day, man was not aware of it. Had they been the size of lions and tigers, or even of cats and dogs, he would have discovered their influence. But being insignificant in size, compared to his, they were ignored.

Man built great temples and altars and made sacrifices to unseen gods. Far better had he made them to placate mosquitoes. Ancient Babylon came near to recognizing them as an enemy. Negral, the Babylonian god of pestilence, was depicted as a double-winged insect resembling the mosquito. Varro, an early Roman, warned farmers not to build their houses on swampy ground because "certain animals, invisible to the human eye, breed there; and, borne by the air, reach the insides of man and cause disease." The present ruins of what was once the splendor of Greece could well be monuments to the mosquito, for malaria was brought to Greece from Africa, where it was endemic, by the slaves. Because of malaria, the citizens of Athens no longer showed initiative. They developed a pessimism in philosophy, a senile aridity in literature, and a morbid brooding over death.

Mosquitoes were responsible for the design of the Roman toga, a garment that could be wrapped around the body to protect it from their stings. Several times mosquitoes saved the city of Rome from being captured by giving malaria to the barbarian hosts camped in the Campagna marshes.

When the Macedonian army marched through the death chamber of Alexander the Great, to bid a silent farewell to the man who had led it in conquering the world, no one suspected that he was dying from the "sword thrust" of a mosquito.

Sir Walter Raleigh, about to die on the gallows, pleaded with his jailers to change the hour of execution to a time when he would not be shaking from malarial fever. He did not want the spectators to think he was shaking with fear.

During the Civil War, in the spring of 1862, when the cry,

"On to Richmond," had carried McClellan's army to the banks of the Chicahominy River, seven miles from the capital, "Chicahominy fever," caused by mosquitoes, so depleted their ranks that General Lee was able to take the initiative.

In World War II, even though their role was known, the sting of mosquitoes caused more casualties in the Southwest Pacific than all the guns and war machines of both Japan and the United States.

In 1872, a serious book called *Health at Home, or Hall's Family Doctor* was published, to "give such information as will enable the most unlettered reader to avail himself of those means of life and health, which nature and Providence have thrown broadcast around him in wonderful profusion."

Doctor Hall never mentions mosquitoes in his book, but gives much space in describing ways for avoiding fevers. He blames them on "miasm," "a result of heat, moisture, and rotting vegetation." He says, "Where there are ponds of stagnant water, there fever and ague abound, attacking individuals and striking down whole families." He insisted that "the operation of the miasmic laws, if studied, are found to be beautifully simple." He tells of a wealthy gentleman who failed to study these laws and built a handsome house in which to spend the summer with his family of growing daughters. He wanted the "country breezes to plant a rosy hue of health on every daughter's cheeks." But soon after they moved into the house, the daughters were struck down with fever. Too late the man discovered "that the breezes with their delicious coolness, morning and evening, blew over a pond of stagnant water and came heavily freighted with miasm."

Doctor Hall conducted a bizarre experiment to prove his miasma theory. At night he filled several barrels with miasma rising from a swamp and having sealed them shipped them a thousand miles north, "where there had never been any fever." The air was released in a bedroom "kept at southern temperature" with all the windows closed. A man was induced to sleep in the room for one night. "He breathed in the miasm, fever got into his lungs, and from them into his bloodstream, and in a short while he came down with chills and fever." The good doctor didn't suspect the mosquito or mosquitoes that had journeyed north in the barrels of miasma.

And in Jamaica, where I spent my early childhood, prior to Mosquito Day miasma was also blamed for our "chills and fever." Our house was situated on the coast. My father called the land breeze, which began to blow at sunset and passed over several inland swamps, "the undertaker," because, he said, it brought the fever with it. We were not allowed to remain outside after it began to blow. The sea breeze, which came in soon after the sun rose, he called "the doctor," because it blew the fevers back into the swamps.

The earliest recorded treatment for fever followed the teachings of Galen, the Greek physician, who believed it was caused by "humors," and could be relieved by purging and bloodletting. And through the following centuries more blood was taken by human "leeches" in their attempts to cure it than by the *Anopheles* for nourishing her eggs.

Mosquitoes influenced the writing of the final scene in Molière's satiric play, *La Malade Imaginaire,* in which a candidate for a doctorate is being examined. The candidate is asked how he would treat a fever. His reply: "Enema first, then bleeding, then purging." Then he was asked, "What if the fever persisted?" His reply: "Re-enema, re-bleed, re-purge."

The curative powers of the bark of the cinchona tree, from which quinine comes, are said to have been discovered by a Spanish soldier left to die of fever in a Peruvian jungle. He drank the water from a small pool, and the fever left him. The water was very bitter. Lightning had struck a cinchona tree overhanging the pool, and the splintered wood and bark had been steeped in the water.

Cinchona bark became a very important Peruvian export, a

monopoly of the Catholic Church. It was instrumental in curing one dauphin of France of malaria and one of the popes, and became known as "Jesuit Bark." When Oliver Cromwell lay dying of malaria, his attendants refused to use it as a cure because it savored of "popery."

For many years the Dutch had a monopoly on growing cinchona trees in the East Indies. They were strict in seeing that none of the seeds were taken out. But a native of Mysore, India, outwitted them. While making love to a Javanese girl in a grove of cinchona trees one night, he left his umbrella, always carried in case of rain, open on the ground and managed to shake the tree in his lovemaking. Some of the seeds fell into the umbrella. He then carried them out of the country in his folded umbrella and planted them in Mysore.

The Dewan of Mysore told me the story when I was a guest there of the Maharaja. He showed me a grove of young cinchona trees that he said had grown from those seeds, and I took photographs of the grove.

Gin and tonic is a drink for which the mosquito is responsible. During the British occupation of India, Europeans were obliged to take daily doses of quinine to ward off malaria, so they mixed the powder in gin to counteract the bitter taste. This is the origin of quinine water.

Through involuntary blood transfusion I have become a part of the mosquito population in the Caribbean, Panama, Central America, the South Pacific, the Philippines, Southeast Asia, India, Ceylon, Australia, New Zealand, the African jungles, Mexico, even Hudson Bay in the far north. In this way I have contributed to the nurturing of their eggs. But it was not until the spring and summer spent at the Wisconsin pond that I began to appreciate the wonder of the mosquito. It was there, while making macrophotographs, that I was able to study them at close range.

I collected mosquito egg rafts from the surface of the pond and kept them in a small aquarium of stagnant water, on the kitchen table in the cabin. I saw them emerge from the eggs as larvae and push their breathing tubes up through the surface. I watched the continually moving cilia combing the water for invisible food. I saw them grow by molting and become shrimp-like pupae breathing air through two tubes that protruded like horns from the sides of their heads. Then I witnessed my first emergence, and this was when my thinking changed.

With an eye dropper I had confined a pupa in a drop of water on a plastic plate. The surface tension of the water made the drop a transparent domed aquarium. I watched the emergence through the magnification of my camera lens, focused an inch away.

A crack opened in the back of the pupal case, and the torso of the mosquito, covered with fine hairs, emerged. The head, with two antennae, a long proboscis, and peacock-blue eyes, quickly followed. Within seconds, a new creature, with wings held closely along the body, stepped daintily on long, graceful legs away from the drop of water and rested on the plastic plate, waiting for its wings to dry.

The smooth proboscis indicated that it was a female. That of the male, who has no need for blood, has feather-like attachments. The proboscis was far from the simple thing it seemed: a tube to be inserted into a pore for drawing blood. It was really an operating instrument, with sharp needles for puncturing skin, a hypodermic needle for injecting saliva into the wound and for drawing blood directly into the mosquito's gut. The saliva had an anticoagulant in it to prevent the blood from clotting. It is with the saliva that the malarial parasites are injected into the human body.

Poised upon the plastic plate was a creature far different in appearance from the shrimp-like form of the pupa out of which I had watched it come. Here was a creature capable of flight, of signaling for a mate, of following the scent of blood to its source, and of obtaining it.

On what loom was the fabric of those gossamer wings woven; in what miniature workshop were those long legs constructed, with nerves and functioning joints; on what emery wheel were the piercing needles sharpened; what boring tool reamed out the tube for drawing blood; on what oculist's wheels were the many lenses of those eyes ground; and from where did the peacock-blue coloring come? Who taught her first to walk and then to fly? Who gave her the secret code by which she communicated? Who made her sensitive to the scent of blood?

Yet all of this had happened within a two-week period and had been produced out of materials present in stagnant water. And plans for this creation had been contained in the tiny egg out of which the "wiggler" had come.

It has well been said that "the greatest miracle in nature is that there is no miracle." All that is seemingly miraculous happens according to a well-established plan.

One night after I had photographed the emergence of a female mosquito on the plastic plate in the kitchen, she followed me up to the loft in which I slept. In the darkness I heard the blood-cry of her whining wings. Holding up my bared arm, I let her take her fill —a model's fee for having posed.

Requiem for an Apple Tree

Trees bridge the gap of time between the vegetable and the animal worlds. When considering them, men have tended to think of them in human terms. The ancients endowed their trees with spirits. Their gods spoke to them through trees.

Jehovah appeared to Abram at the oak of Moreh, and God spoke to Moses out of a burning bush. On a hunting safari, which I photographed in Mozambique, Africa, the trackers in our party who were unable to locate the elephants stopped beneath a tree in which they believed the spirit of one of their dead chiefs lived. They made an offering of mealie meal and tobacco spread on leaves at the base of the tree and in a singsong chant, while clapping their hands, told the chief that they had brought gifts and pleaded with him to tell them how to find the elephants. They then changed the direction in which we had been traveling. In less than thirty minutes, we came upon a herd of elephants.

Poets get sentimental when they write about trees:

"A tree that looks to God all day, and lifts her leafy arms to pray."

"They bravely stand in the silent wood, like a patient life that is nobly good."

"Jack Frost removes their robes of leaves, to show their naked loveliness against the western sky."

"The talking of the leaves dies down, except for a few persistent ones, who keep going on in whispers."

"Green-robed dancers doing their turns against the setting sun."

I, too, became sentimental about one of the remaining apple trees where once an orchard had been. It was near the ruins of the barn and was dying. There was little life left in it when I arrived in April. The center of the trunk had long since rotted away, leaving a hollow shell of bark, wrinkled with age. It was scarred and pockmarked with countless holes that generations of woodpeckers, sapsuckers, and other birds had drilled in their search for grubs. Life had left all but one branch. A narrow strip of bark still carried nourishment to it from the earth, and the few leaves on it took sustenance from the sunlight.

I didn't know whether certain sections of the bark on trees fed certain limbs, or whether the food gathered by the roots was communal, to be shared equally by all. But the strip of bark remaining on that tree was on the same side of the trunk as the living branch.

Late in April, as it had for many decades, the branch sprouted leaves and buds, and eventually apple blossoms. There were not many blossoms, but they were the pearly-pink of apple blossoms. Their scent was apple-sweet, and bees and other insects visited them. Compared to blossoms from younger trees they seemed the same. But when they faded and the petals fell, no tiny apples took their place. The fruit-bearing period of that tree had passed.

Late in August a strange thing happened; a second set of buds appeared on the lone branch of the old apple tree. The flowers again were pearly-pink and fragrant as the ones in April had been, but the second blossoming quickly faded.

I thought of a piece in the poem, "My Grandfather's Clock":

Rang an alarm in the midst of the night;
An alarm that for years had been dumb;

Then we knew that its spirit was pluming for flight,
That the hour of departure had come.

The leaves on the branch soon followed the faded flowers, and before frost arrived, the old tree had died. The last living vestige of the orchard had succumbed to a cycle of life. Bit by bit it would rot and decay, to become again part of the soil.

Insects

There was no way of telling how many insects inhabited the pond and the area about it. It takes two acres of ordinary farmland to support one cow, but it has been estimated that a single acre of land, covered with vegetation, can support eight million insects!

Insects are one of the most successful classes of animals. Over six hundred thousand different types have been identified. It is estimated that there are two to four million others. The majority of adult insects are so small they do not attract the human eye. Despite our modern insecticides, they will probably be on earth long after man has departed. They were present in the coal age, three hundred million years before man appeared on earth. Evolution has dealt lavishly with them in producing so many kinds. Mutation, which causes a different "life-thing" to emerge and which occurs only once in ten thousand births, has had a free rein in the insect world because of insects' massive reproductive capacity.

The brain of an insect is perhaps the most highly organized bit of living matter in the animal kingdom. Contained within its microscopic confines are the vast neural patterns that direct the insect's intricate behavior from the moment of its birth until its death. These patterns are a biological summation of all the experiments of the species through uncountable generations of living.

They are the end results of trial and error on a vast ancestral proving ground. The length of man's experiments in living compared to that of insects' is but a drop of water in time's boundless sea.

Each insect species is a relic of one of life's experiments that culminated in a dead end of perfection. This development ensures the survival of the species, but provides no opportunity for change. A hunting wasp will never learn the art of paper-making; nor a paper-maker wasp the fine technique needed for paralyzing a caterpillar to keep it alive for larval food.

Insects are biologically adult when they emerge from the pupae. The abilities they have at the time of death are those they possessed at the beginning of their lives. For them there is no babyhood, no adolescence for learning, no old age where wisdom ripens. And lacking the many storage cells in their brain required for memory and the multiple cross-fibers that, in the brains of higher animals, permit learning, insects are able to learn very little.

Insects need no special minerals for building bones. No proteins for the glands that, in higher animals, determine the rate of growth, size, color, temperament, length of life, and ability to mate. Their food problem is one of obtaining sufficient amounts to furnish energy, to manipulate organs, and, in some species, to succor the larvae that hatch out of the eggs they lay.

Under an ordinary microscope the speck of matter that is the brain of an ant resembles the speck directing the activities of a wasp. But the patterns in the two brains, spread out as blueprints, are vastly different. The patterns governing their walking movements are somewhat similar. But the wasp needs additional patterns for flight, not only patterns to ensure that wings vibrate to keep them aloft, but also patterns that determine pitch and relative velocity of each wing, so that they carry the wasp along a necessary path of flight. A wasp unable to change directions while in flight would be in the same predicament as the ant that could walk only in a straight line.

In observing the motions of an ant, it becomes obvious that the movement of the legs is synchronized, each moving in relation to the ones next to it. If some legs moved in one direction and others in another, there would be confusion and the ant couldn't survive. When an ant turns to the right, the legs on that side must take fewer or shorter steps than those on the left. The differential gear in an automobile is designed to compensate for the differing speeds of the wheels when the car is turning a corner. The ant possesses a biological means of accomplishing the same result.

There are other much more complicated patterns than motor movement needed to keep the species alive. There are patterns that direct the senses of sight and smell, directing how much is to be eaten on the spot and what should be stored for feeding larvae or for winter food. Leaf-cutting ants need special patterns by which to know what leaves to choose, and once they have cut sections from the leaves, other patterns by which to know how to store them in the proper atmosphere to produce the fungus upon which they feed.

There are ants that milk the honey from aphids, which must be carried by the ants to the right kind of tree for pasture, the way a farmer does his milch cows.

And somewhere in the great time-vastness of the paper-making wasp's heredity, patterns for making paper from decayed wood and other patterns for constructing the cells were incorporated. These would be somewhat like the patterns bees use for constructing their cells. In terms of shape, the cells are alike. The cell-making patterns of the paper-maker are simpler than those of the mud daubers, the wasps that build clumsy cells of clay. Still simpler yet are the patterns by which the solitary wasp excavates her nest-hole in the ground. But she would need a very special set of "surgeon's" blueprints to enable her to locate the nerve centers in the caterpillar that she anesthetizes to keep it alive for larval food. And none of this information is taught to wasp or bee. They do not make practice cells before beginning the finished ones.

There are some patterns of insect behavior which could not have been established by trial and error in their past. Try capturing an ant, and note his tactics for evading you. He makes quick use of any bits of the surroundings under which to hide. Then watch a spider constructing a web that will stretch across an area that she has not seen before. Note how she fastens the guy lines, as though being directed to different points. Both insects' actions are tactics used in dealing with completely new situations.

Our thinking has been governed by the patterns responsible for the behavior of the complete insect. Refinement in thinking suggests that each living cell within the insect must have its individual blueprint of behavior for the construction of the different organs in the creature. And of all the insects about the pond, the honeybee would need the most extensive set of neural blueprints to direct the complicated social manner of life that the species has evolved.

Through the ages much thought has been given by scientists and philosophers to animal behavior, especially to that of insects. They have come up with the suspect term "instinct" to describe it. Although they differ as to what they mean by instinct, most scientists recognize in insects a subtle and mysterious form of control, which suggests actions and systems of actions that indicate the employment of definite means to an end without the intervention of a chain of thought—a process that in human beings characterizes reason. But they have found it difficult to decide how far intelligence modifies instinct, and instinct stimulates intelligence.

The law of instinct is the law of the living principle. It is neither essential mind nor essential matter. It is neither passion nor sensation. Though unquestionably distinct from all of these, it is capable of combining with any of them. Instinct is possessed with its own book of laws, to which, under the same circumstances, it adheres without the smallest deviation. Its sole and uniform aim, whether acting generally or locally, is that of health, preservation, and reproduction.

It has been called "Emanations from the Deity." The late zoologist William Morton Wheeler felt that: "Human intellect abdicates when it is called upon to grasp an activity that is unconsciously purposeful." He also said that "the thing we call instinct may transcend intelligence and have its mainspring in the depths of the life process itself." And: "An instinct is more or less complicated activity manifested by an organism which is acting first, as a whole rather than a part; second, as the representative of a species rather than as an individual; third, without previous experience; and fourth, with an end, or purpose of which it has no knowledge."

Rene Thevenin said: "Instinct is an immutable property of living matter transmitted to creatures by a supernatural power, to insure their conservation, irrespective of their own interests. These creatures have no consciousness of it and cannot modify it in any way. It alone knows its ends and makes directly for them."

The Living Picture Window

On a wooden platform, under the poplar tree behind the cabin, I had a living picture window. Contained between the plate-glass sides of a large aquarium was a cross section of the pond. In it I could observe the living things close-up, as though seated in a glass compartment sunk in the pond.

Water plants were growing from the muck in the bottom of the aquarium. Water lilies and duckweed floated on the surface. In the center was a section of a sunken log, with crevices in which pond creatures laid their eggs. In one corner was a large moss-covered stone.

There were many creatures in this window. Some were graceful; some grotesque. They swam about; they dived; and they crawled. Some were hunters; others were hunted. All were adapted to pond living, and though they varied in shape and size, they were constructed from the same basic pond elements. This miniature pond, like the larger one from which the creatures came, was a self-sufficient unit of life. It provided food for all the creatures living in it.

Whenever I approached the picture window, there was much frantic movement. Some of the occupants scurried about in vain efforts to escape. Others cleverly concealed themselves under the leaves of the water plants. If I remained still, they soon ignored me, and went about their business of living in a normal manner.

Among the submerged roots of a willow near the old beaver dam, I found a crayfish. One of her great fighting claws was missing. The new one had not begun developing. The underside of her abdomen was clean and shiny. At first I thought it was a new shell she had recently "changed" into, after sloughing off the old. But the shell on her back was moss-encrusted. I realized then that she was a pregnant female who had cleaned off her underside for depositing her eggs.

I placed her on the moss-covered stone in the picture window. From it she could reach her head above the surface whenever she needed air.

She laid her eggs during the night, and I missed seeing the event. She had turned over on her back, and the eggs had poured out from special openings at the base of her third pair of legs. She had rolled from side to side while they were coming out, so that they would be evenly distributed. An adhesive on each egg firmly fastened it to a swimmeret. The next morning she was standing on the moss-covered stone, her body and tail elevated, her swimmerets slowly waving back and forth to aerate the eggs. It was weeks before they hatched, and during all of that time she kept the swimmerets moving.

When the young came out of the eggs, they did not swim away, but remained attached. Using a soda straw, I sucked some of them up. They were so small that three could swim about in a single drop of water on a dry pine board, a miniature aquarium.

Here was another example of nature's mysterious perfection. Each tiny mite was a complete creature, with all the functional parts of the adult. And it had all been developed in the egg.

One morning I watched the nymph of a dragonfly, perched

on a water plant, just inches from the glass. No need had he for a breathing tube to reach up through the surface for air like the larvae of mosquitoes, nor to collect a supply of air in a bubble like the whirligigs. He was equipped with a special chamber, with walls lined with a network of air tubes. With these he extracted the oxygen directly from the water, the way fish do with their gills. I could see his abdomen contracting and expanding as he "breathed." The nymph could survive indefinitely underwater. But if he never left the pond, there would be no future nymphs. The mysterious scheme of life decrees that he must go through metamorphosis and become a dragonfly before he can mate and reproduce his kind.

Suddenly he expelled the water from this breathing tube and darted forward, jet-propelled, and perched on the stem of another plant near which a hog-nosed minnow was swimming. There the posture of the nymph changed. A tenseness gripped him, and he crouched low on the stem to be less conspicuous. His head, in which were two large compound eyes, each with several thousand smaller eyes, followed the movement of the minnow, and he slowly crawled along the stem until he reached a point near which the minnow would pass, and there he waited.

This nymph was following the basic hunting pattern of all predators. It is the pattern followed by a cat stalking a bird or mouse, a jumping spider creeping up upon a fly, a lioness preparing to spring upon an antelope. Quite probably, it was the same crouching, creeping pattern that was followed by an early caveman hunting with a club.

Unlike the spider, cat, or lioness, the nymph will not spring upon its prey. The designer of nymphs has equipped him with a unique prehensile jaw, folded out of sight in a groove below his head. This jaw, when extended, is nearly as long as the nymph. It is equipped with four curved, needle-sharp points. Not only can the jaw shoot out and sink the points in prey as large as the minnow, but the jaw can also be used to capture water fleas, which are barely visible to the human eye.

Unaware of the lurking danger, the minnow swam within range. The jaw shot out, sinking the points deep in the minnow, just behind its dorsal fin. The movement was too rapid for me to follow. With frantic twists and turns, the minnow tried to shake its captor loose, but the jaw held fast, and the nymph hung on while the minnow dashed out across the aquarium.

Like needles of a hypodermic syringe, the curved points of the jaw are hollow. Through them the nymph injected an anesthetic that quickly stopped the minnow's struggling. Then it perched on another plant, fastened its toes securely in the stem, and began to feed.

The fluid that had paralyzed the minnow also contained an ingredient that dissolved the tissues. The nymph fed by drawing the liquefied flesh through the second pair of "needles." Unlike the dragonfly, the nymph has no mouth parts, and must depend upon food that has been liquefied.

In less than half an hour, only the head and backbone of the minnow remained. Finally, the nymph let go of them and "jetted" away. The remains sank and lay upon the bottom. Another minnow, attracted by the odor of raw flesh, began feeding on them. He grasped a piece, then tore it loose by violent twistings of his tail. A crayfish had also picked up the scent. It moved slowly toward the carcass, brandishing a large fighting claw. This claw, though seemingly clumsy, could slash out with lightning speed and capture fish. Aware of the potential danger, the minnow swam away, leaving the crayfish to feed alone.

Small pincers on the front legs of the crayfish tore off tiny bits of the minnow flesh and passed them along to the crayfish's mouth. The mouth is vertical and is composed of several moving segments with teeth in them. They operated in a rotary rhythm as they ground up the flesh.

While the crayfish was feeding on the dead minnow, a wheeled snail was feeding upon the algae collected on the crayfish's back.

The whirligig beetles in my picture window were figure skaters. They seemed to delight in cutting intricate designs upon the surface of the aquarium as they went about collecting food. Their favorite food was the flies I caught and crushed for them. When one went below to hide among the plant leaves, it would take with it a supply of air in a bubble attached to the tip of its body and remain below until the air was exhausted.

There were many beetles in the picture window. Most numerous was a small one with brown spots. They are the scavengers that search among the muck on the bottom for bits of food discarded by the other creatures. When one needed air, it would dart to the surface and, like a whirligig, collect it in a bubble. The sunlight shining on these bubbles as they flashed through the water converted them into lovely streaks of silver.

The largest beetle in the pond was a dytiscus, over two inches long. His glistening wing cases were a dark brown with a stripe of yellow along the edges. He fed upon minnows, nymphs, and tadpoles, and upon earthworms and bits of raw meat I sometimes put in the tank for a treat. When at rest, he hung downward at an angle, the tip of his body projecting through the surface for collecting air. The nymph he came from was the water tiger, the most ferocious creature in the pond. It resembled the mythical picture of a dragon. It had curved jaws like the nymph of the dragonfly, and sank them into the soft undersides of tadpoles, sucking out the body juices, leaving only the shrunken skin. It was the creature that "attacked" me when I picked it up from the shaker-board.

Tadpoles were the most numerous creatures in the picture window. They were the easiest to dredge out of the pond and a good source of food. Nymphs, beetles, and water scorpions capture them alive. Minnows, leeches, and snails feed on the remnants.

Yet a tadpole's changing into a frog provides much food for thought. It is one of the great miracles in nature. The original change took millions of years to perfect and proceeded in slow stages. In my picture window I could see it taking place in days.

A tadpole is essentially a fish with a tail, gills for getting oxygen directly from the water, lidless eyes, and a mouth suited to nibbling water plants and feeding upon algae. It excretes waste material, as ammonia, into the water. Its skin is thin, and if exposed to air, the body moisture seeps through it and quickly the animal becomes dehydrated. In the water, it is herbivorous, with a long intestine.

Then, through metamorphosis, it changes into a terrestrial creature, with a thick skin to resist evaporation, air-breathing lungs instead of gills, eyelids, a mouth, a tongue, and four legs with powerful muscles. It becomes a carnivore, with a short intestine, an eater of insects and other invertebrate animals. The tail is absorbed, and body waste is excreted as urea.

At first a tadpole is content to live among the other aquatic creatures. Then two legs begin sprouting at the base of its tail. The tail gets shorter, and two front legs begin to grow. Raised eye sockets form, and the tadpole takes on the resemblance of a frog. More of its time begins to be spent near the water's surface, and as its lungs develop, it begins breathing air. When the metamorphosis is completed, it crawls out on a lily pad and waits for passing insects.

A most unusual thing about a frog is the way it sees. The frog's eye is not an instrument like a camera, with a lens and a recording film of nerves, as in other animals. In the frog it is a biological instrument, a "bug detector," developed to meet the animal's need. It "sees" only small moving objects that come within range of the darting tongue. These objects are normally insects, but a frog will "strike" at any small object waved in front of its eyes. A frog would starve to death surrounded by insects that did not move. If they were still, it would not be able to see them. Frog eyes, which are sensitive to the color blue, assist in the frog's survival. When in the weeds or grass beside the pond, and suddenly startled by a hunting raccoon or heron or other animal, the frog will automatically jump toward the blue of the sky or water, and thus escape. If it jumped toward green—the grass or weeds—it would be easily captured.

Another advantage the frog has is that its eyes, like those of birds, are equipped with nictitating eyelids, transparent inner lids that move up from below and cover the pupils to protect them when the frog dives under water.

I cut an earthworm in sections and dropped it in the picture window. "Word" quickly spread through waves of scent in the water, and several things began to happen. A large section of the worm landed in the branches of a water plant, and a unique pair of creatures were attracted. The first to reach it was a water scorpion. It had long slender legs, which were not designed for swimming. They gave it a grotesque motion as it moved toward the worm. Its head was small, with two large, protruding eyes. Two long, jointed "arms" go out from it, each with a curved point at the end. With these it pulled the worm closer. Then it sank its beak into it and sucked out the juices. Meanwhile, the tip of a long, thin, hair-like tube extended up through the surface, and through this it "breathed" the needed air.

The other creature in this feeding twosome was a male water bug, an inch in length. He too sank a beak into the worm, but not having a breathing tube, he had to push the end of his body up through the surface. Glued to his back by the female were scores of upright eggs. These require ten days to hatch, and during all of this time he is obliged to carry them with him wherever he goes, so they will be properly aerated.

A number of small, bright red spots among the eggs of the water bug are those of a water mite, a distant relative of the spider. They, too, will be aerated, along with the others.

In the beginning there were six small bass in the picture window. One by one they disappeared, but the lone survivor grew much larger. Because of his sinister look and his depredations, I named him "The Gangster." He would eat worms, but preferred fish, especially bass. He swallowed them headfirst so that the barbs of their dorsal fins would not become lodged in his throat.

Fish, like birds and other animals, including insects, tend to follow the solunar feeding periods, as was evident in the way the bass and other fish fed. The Gangster would be swimming contentedly among the smaller minnows and other fish, as though unconscious of their presence. Then the feeding period would arrive, and he would suddenly dart out and capture one. If he was very hungry, he would eat three or four.

Putting the pieces of worms in the aquarium seemed to upset this feeding rhythm, for the catfish anyway. There were eighteen when I first dredged them out of the pond. I thought they were newly hatched toad tadpoles. They were the same size and color, black. But when I picked one up between my thumb and forefinger, the spikes behind his head punctured my skin, and I realized that they were catfish. Within a week only a dozen remained. Their soft bodies had been devoured by the nymphs and the dytiscus beetle. Because of the spikes and the poison in them, the heads were left uneaten.

The catfish stayed together in a school, as they had done in the pond. In the pond, they would follow the mother about as young chicks do a hen. The mother catfish stirs up the muck along the bottom, and the young search among it for food. The hen scratches the soil, turning up bits of food for the chicks.

The catfish sense of smell is very acute. One of the most successful baits used by commercial fishermen is a concoction containing aged cheese. Moments after I had put the sections of the earthworm into the aquarium, the young catfish became aware of it, although they were several feet away from where the sections landed. Like a pack of hounds, they spread out quickly and followed the scent to its source. One of them grabbed the end of a small worm section and tried to swallow it. But it was too big a mouthful. Another one grabbed the other end, and there was a tug-of-war. The first won and swam away with the worm protruding from his mouth. He looked as though he was smoking a cigar. But he was not allowed to eat it. Several others ganged up on him, and there was another tussle. I could imagine underwater snarling as they fought for it. The first one had it partly swallowed when a minnow dashed up and took the worm away. The catfish then discovered another piece of worm, and the battle began again.

Feeding the creatures in my picture window was very simple. One drag of my wire scoop across the bottom of the pond collected a large variety of food. Sometimes I would pull up a root of watercress from the spring and put that in the tank. Hundreds of small crustaceans would scatter from it, and there would be a feast.

By the end of summer, when I left the pond, all of the dragonfly nymphs had emerged and departed. The tadpoles had changed to frogs and toads, and I released them. The Gangster bass was several inches long. There were only five catfish remaining; they had grown to over an inch in length. The crayfish, too, had grown. I had often watched them when they "changed" to a larger shell. I brought a few of the creatures back home with me: the female crayfish, the catfish, The Gangster, and the dytiscus beetle. I kept them in an aquarium in the kitchen and fed them through the winter on worms. The others were put back in the pond.

I'd often play at fishing with the bass. He'd strike at artificial bass-fishing lures, minus the hooks. And once in a while I'd give him a treat of guppies purchased from a local pet shop. The dytis-cus lasted through most of the winter. One of his favorite foods was bits of raw hamburger. One morning in January I found him dead. He was floating in the customary position, head down and tail end up against the surface. The crayfish drowned. I had a special wire screen on which he could crawl to push his head above the surface when he needed air. One night he got caught on the underside and couldn't get out. When spring came, the catfish were released in a small pond in the Indiana dunes, and The Gangster in a nearby stream.

The Bees

Honey and the work of bees have been associated with the life of man since the beginning of human history. Bees fertilized the flower of the tree "in the midst of the garden" that produced the fruit Eve used to tempt Adam. The Pile Dwellers of the Swiss lakes, the earliest people known to build permanent houses, had utensils for separating honey from beeswax. The pharaohs got their sweets from honey. Byati, meaning "beekeeper," was the title of the Egyptian kings. Honey also helped preserve their bodies after death.

Beeswax was used by Aristophanes for writing and for sealing his famous love letters. Alexander the Great, by his request, was buried in combs of virgin honey. The Incas offered honey in their sacrifices to the Sun God. The name, Vishnu, the early religious leader of the Hindus, means, in Sanskrit, "one born in honey."

Candles made from beeswax have been used for centuries in the ceremonies of the church. The virginity of the bees was symbolic of the flesh of Christ, born of a virgin mother.

Royal jelly, a mysterious food product of bees that is believed to be responsible for the development of queens instead of workers if fed to the larvae in their early stages, is used in France by men as an aphrodisiac. It is also used in face creams by women, to make them more attractive to men.

On sunny days, the bees were my companions as I roamed about the pond. I marveled at the perfection of their development. But, as time passed, and I continued observing them, my conclusions changed. No longer did I see them as free creatures, like butterflies, flitting from flower to flower, collecting nourishment for their individual needs. Instead, I saw them as dominated female slaves, forbidden to mate and lay eggs, forced to produce vast quantities of food beyond their personal needs, food that was stored in hives to produce future colonies of emasculated slaves.

The workers, in the early larval stage, are all potential queens. But the cells in which they develop are small, and a restricted diet stunts their growth. When they emerge from the cells as bees, they are exposed to a mysterious substance that the queen secretes; this substance inhibits the development of their ovaries and their ability to manufacture the larger cells in which new queens are reared.

Through the use of this pheromone, produced in her mandibular glands, the queen controls the activity of the colony. In that sense she can be called a queen. But, in actual practice, she is but a superslave, dominated in turn by the workers. Despite Maeterlinck and E. B. White's "Song of the Bee," her life is far from being a romantic one. She mates but once and then spends the rest of her life, night and day, laying eggs.

The pheromone, which inhibits the workers, also serves the queen as a sex attraction in her nuptial flight. She excretes it as she leaves the hive and spirals upward. It stimulates the sex activity in the drones and creates a path by which they follow her. The strongest flier overtakes her, and they mate high in the air. His genital organs remain in the queen, and soon after mating with her, he dies. In a special sac below her ovaries the queen carries back to the hive the millions of sperm she has received from him, sufficient numbers to fertilize all the eggs she will lay. It is estimated that a

queen will lay a thousand eggs a day and can continue at that pace for many months.

As soon as she returns to the hive, bringing with her the genitals of the drone, evidence that she has mated, a retinue of workers takes charge. They keep her clean and bring her food and see that she continues laying eggs. She dare not falter. If she does, they gang up on her and do what beekeepers call "balling the queen."

The balling is started by a single worker's pulling at a leg or wing of the queen. The worker also exudes a pheromone that instantly incites the bees next to her, and they, too, join in the attack, also exuding the substance. In seconds, hundreds of other bees join the mob, each one trying to get at the queen. She remains in the center of the ball of excited bees and is eventually squeezed to death.

Sociologists have been intrigued by the similarity of mob behavior in bees and human beings. In bees, the action is set off by a single individual and quickly spreads to others. Patterns of behavior are released that would not normally be tolerated by the individuals.

When the queen is dead, her pheromone control ends, and the workers, freed from its domination, begin manufacturing the larger cells in which to rear new queens. The walls of three normal cells are torn down to accommodate the larger queen cell. With no restrictions on them, some of the workers begin laying eggs. This is but a futile gesture, for they have not been fertilized, and the eggs they lay can produce only drones.

In size and texture, the queen cells in a hive resemble unshelled peanuts. They stand out above the others and are covered with a thicker layer of wax. A dozen or more of them are built. The first queen to emerge immediately searches out the other queen cells, cuts through the protecting wax, and stings her potential rivals to death. If two emerge at the same time, there is a battle until one of them is killed.

It is intriguing that the emerging queen is aware of the other queens still sealed in their cells, aware of the potential danger to her sovereignty.

There are conflicting ideas as to what makes an ordinary fertile egg develop into a queen instead of a worker. The enlarged cell is one clue, making possible a greater amount of larval food. But once the queen substance, which inhibits the workers from building the queen cells, is removed and the larger cells are manufactured and young larvae installed, royal jelly, the essential components of which have not been identified, becomes necessary for their development into the queen caste.

Drones are the only members of the honeybee colony that seem to benefit from the highly organized social state. They live like proper gentlemen. When they are hungry, a passing worker feeds them. On sunny days drones leave the hive for constitutional flights. They never work. Sufficient numbers of them are produced to ensure the fertilization of a new queen if that becomes necessary. But their carefree living ends when the flow of nectar diminishes at the end of summer. They are nonproductive members that would have to be fed during the winter months on the stored food. Somehow, the word is passed that they are no longer welcome. One day, when they return from their flights, a group of workers meets them at the entrance to the hive. Two workers grab them, one on each side, and ride them down to the ground. Drones cannot sting, and therefore they cannot defend themselves. Never having learned how to gather food, they starve or are eaten by the toads and other creatures waiting below the hive to feed upon the weary and heavy-laden bees that fall off the hive landing board.

Drones are produced in special cells slightly larger than those of the workers but built on the same pattern. Theirs are not like the peanut-shaped, outstanding cells that the queens are developed in.

And in these cells the queen lays a nonfertile egg! Here is another seeming mystery in the life of the bee. How does the queen know where to lay her fertile and where her nonfertile eggs? All egg-laying is done in total darkness. One explanation is that when the queen is laying the fertile egg, her abdomen is compressed by the size of the cell—the size and shape of the other cells in a honeybee comb never vary—and the egg, passing from the ovary, is forced to pass through the sac in which the male sperm are stored. When an egg is deposited in the larger drone cell, the abdomen is not compressed, and the egg bypasses the sperm sac.

This makes the drone a unique creature. Coming from an unfertilized egg, he has no father. But he does have a mother, and a grandfather on his mother's side!

When two queens survive in a hive, one of them, the weaker, will take a part of the colony with her out on "swarm," to find new quarters. The swarming procedure is suggestive of the early colonizing of human beings. The bees start out prepared, as though knowing they are going on a journey. Each fills its honey stomach with an extra supply, so that it will have material for making wax to build the cells of its new home, as well as for nourishment. Several drones will also be taken along to ensure the fertility of a new queen should some accident befall the old one.

The swarm locates upon some object not far from the original hive and sends out fifty to a hundred scouts to investigate likely places for a new home. As the scouts return, by interpretive dance steps and perhaps by sounds they indicate what they have found. The intensity of the dance indicates how favorable the site is. The bees decide upon one site and follow the scouts to it, and there they begin constructing their new home.

After a busy day, when much nectar, which contains water, has been collected, the moisture content of the hive gets high. Unless this moisture content is reduced, fermentation will take place. The high moisture content triggers a set of ingrained behavior patterns, as water rising in a basement activates a sump pump. The bees line up in rows at the entrance to the hive and set their wings in motion. Some face inward and blow the moist air out; others face outward and fan in dry air.

Numerous bee behavior patterns are difficult for human thinking to explain. The most difficult to understand is the dance by which the bees inform the others of the discovery of a new source of nectar. By a series of interpretive movements, which have been charted by scientists, they give directions that other bees can follow. Through the medium of the dance also, they indicate the amount of the find. Recent research has also discovered that, in addition to dancing, the bees make sounds—a language of the bees —which have been tape-recorded.

Young bees that emerge from the cell at the end of their larval period are not taught. They know. Their brain, the size of a pinhead, is not capable of thinking. All of the activities necessary in so complicated an organization result from innate patterns of behavior impressed upon their nervous system over the immense reaches of time during their phylogenetic development.

There is no greater evidence accounting for the length of time that life has been active on the earth than the activities of the bees. It is humbling indeed to consider the time that was necessary to establish the behavior patterns of bees. There has been no evidence of change in these patterns throughout human history.

The first three days of a worker's life are spent cleaning the brood cells by licking the surface with her tongue. She leaves an odor that informs the queen that the cell has been cleaned and is ready to receive the egg. The queen inserts her head in every cell before laying, and if the odor is not present, she will not deposit the egg. After the egg has been laid, the workers attending the queen investigate the cell to ensure that the egg has been properly attached.

The worker's pharyngeal glands secrete a substance that,

mixed with pollen and honey, produces "bee-milk," the early food of the developing larvae. Rearing a single larva requires two to three thousand visits of the foster mother to supply this bee-milk. When the pharyngeal glands degenerate, a worker can no longer be a "nursemaid." Her duties then are to store the nectar and pollen brought in by the "field bees." If these glands did not degenerate, the worker might spend her entire life feeding larvae.

New worker bees also act as guards at the hive entrance to prevent bees from other colonies entering and stealing the honey. Bees secrete an odor peculiar to their colony, a kind of "password" that gives them entrance. During their period as guards, the young bees go out on short flights of orientation, recognizing landmarks that will enable them to locate the hive when they become full-fledged field bees.

In a busy season a field bee will wear herself out in four or five weeks. She must visit a thousand to fifteen hundred flowers to refill her honey-stomach. This stomach is the communal one, and the contents of it belong to the colony. The personal stomach of the bee is just below it. An automatic valve admits sufficient nectar to it to satisfy her nutritional needs. When she dies, her body is carted some distance from the hive and dropped.

The stinger of a honeybee is barbed. That of the queen is not; barbs are not needed in the performance of her tasks. Like the penis of the drone, which remains in the queen with which he mates and the loss of which causes his death, the stinger of the worker remains in the object stung. And she, too, dies. Both worker and drone are sacrificed to the welfare of the colony. In death the drone provides the sperm. And when the stinger of the worker is pulled out of her body, a special scent gland is ruptured. This quickly spreads an alarm through the air, alerting the other bees of danger, and they follow the scent and attack the enemy.

The six-walled cell of a honeycomb is the strongest form of

construction possible. It is also the most efficient shape for storing the honey, and the bees were never taught how to build it. The cells are slanted, and this, aided by the mysterious capillary attraction, prevents the honey from running out. The wax from which they are made is secreted from wax glands on the bee's underside. It comes out as a liquid, dries into tiny flakes, and is molded into cell walls by the bee's mandibles. Seven pounds of honey are used to make a single pound of wax!

A colony of honeybees is a functional unit of life, and though larger, it is as basic as a living cell. Both have their integrating parts that cooperate to function as the whole. Both exist in an infinity of space and time.

As I continued to observe and meditate about the bees around the pond, I wondered why the writer of the Book of Proverbs had not included them in his list of things too wonderful for him to comprehend. He mentions four: "The way of an eagle in the air; the way of a serpent upon a rock; the way of a ship in the midst of the sea; and the way of a man with a maid." A honeybee could well have been a fifth. For they were there when he was writing the Proverbs, and their way of life had been perfected aeons earlier.

The Oak

High up on the sloping hillside above the abandoned field, the trunk of an immense oak lay rotting. The elements life had used to grow the tree were, through decay, being returned to the earth. A jagged stump indicated where the tree had once stood before the force of wind had snapped it off. In the center of the stump, among the rot of wood and leaves, another oak had already started growing.

In human terminology, the tree had suffered an accidental death; it had occurred on the day of the windstorm. But death had been ever present in the tree. The process that produced it had been a continuing one of dying. New, living cells built upon the corpses of the old. They too died soon after they were formed.

Life in the tree had been but a series of exploding powder trains. The first began to burn within the acorn out of which the oak had come. Fertilization had been the match that touched it off. That giant oak, rising above the other trees in all its majesty, had been but one of life's monuments to death. And I, a human being, was but another one.

While considering the oak and its long life and looking at the rotting remnants on the ground, I recalled a pageant for a doctor put on in a small Wisconsin town. He had been the only doctor there for thirty years. He treated all the human ills of the townspeople. He had brought into the world over three thousand babies. The pageant was to show the people's gratitude, when, because of his age, he could no longer serve them. His patients down through the years paraded down Main Street where his office was always located. The doctor sat on a platform and greeted them. Among the marchers were hundreds of the babies he had delivered, now grown, many of them carrying babies of their own.

The oak also deserved a pageant to mark its contribution. Nature's many creatures who in their lifetime had benefited by the oak's presence might well acknowledge their debt to the old tree. Those still living mingling with the resurrected dead. Not passing two by two, male and his female, but in groups, by species, each saluting the oak in its peculiar way.

Using the magic wand of imagination, I could see the pageant take form, the participants parading past the oak, once again erect, standing on the hillside.

The early morning was set aside for spiders. All that had spun webs upon the tree and on the bushes below it returned to spin again. Each web was outlined by the drops of dew. The rising sun, shining on them, turned them into pearls, and as the heat increased, the pearls changed into vapor, rising as jeweled incense to the tree.

The tasseled flowers of the oak then shyly showed themselves again. A breeze rose from the pond and shook the tree, and a golden shower of pollen grains burst forth. These fell upon the female counterparts of the flowers, and life was once again renewed. Then in the twinkling of an eye the leaves unfurled, dressing the oak in veils of light green beauty.

Next came the insects. The simple types laid their eggs upon the leaves and bark and left them there to hatch into pupae, then, through the mysteries of metamorphosis, to become the new adults. The more sophisticated insects, gallflies, made use of the young

leaves' abundant sap for forming galls in which to lay their eggs. Still more sophisticated ones with long, steel-tipped ovipositories probed through the fibers of the tree's tough wood to deposit their eggs on moth larvae boring deep below the bark.

The myriad insect wings of varying size and shape, each vibrating at a different speed, some high-pitched, others low, beat the air in unison, making music which enveloped the oak.

Then came caterpillars, hatching from insect eggs, both the smooth-skinned and the hairy, the bright colored and the dull, but all crawling upon the tree. Some spun cocoons of silken thread; others made chrysalides of chitin. The metamorphic space of time was filled with the flutter of wings of creatures that the oak had time. Moths mingled with the butterflies. The sky about the oak was filled with the flutter of wings of creatures that the oak had once spawned and nurtured.

The sanitary corps of restless ants who, throughout all the years, ranged over the tree both day and night in search of bits of food discarded by the other creatures also returned. They swarmed over the trunk and limbs in nervous close-packed ranks, and as they moved, the tree became a thing alive.

The birds came, too. The crows were first. Arriving in a vast flock, they blacked out the sunlight and filled the woods with shade, and in a single voice sounded their combined noises of all the years in one stupendous caw.

The hawks' salute was one of flight, a revelry of aerobatics. Redoing all the swoops and rolls and dives that they had performed when, for them, the oak had been a high vantage point from which to spot their prey.

After the crows and hawks had departed, the sharp-billed birds arrived. Woodpeckers of assorted size and hue, many with red heads, and flickers, too—all who had once searched beneath the bark for food hung in spirals around the tree, with beaks upraised, and all began to drill at once. Trip-hammers vibrated through the woods and filled the air with flying debris, confetti for the pageant.

Then came the smaller birds, warblers, creepers, nuthatches, who in their seasonal migrations had visited the oak and scoured the bark and scratched among the fallen leaves for insects to sustain them on their strenuous flights. They did their prancings, up and down, encasing the tree in a warm robe of feathers.

Next, all the birds that hatched from nests returned. The robins, blackbirds, blue jays, orioles, and mourning doves. They did their fledgling flights again and, bursting from their countless nests, produced a display of feathered fireworks.

After the birds had gone, the squirrels came: the reds, the grays. Where the feathered coat had earlier been, now there was one of fur. Then, like a motion picture running backward, the acorns that had fallen from the tree sprang up and filled the hairy cups. The squirrels cut them off again, and they fell like hail and lay foot deep upon the ground in recognition of the oak's fertility.

All the deer that had fed on the acorns came to feed again. They rubbed their sides against the tree to rid themselves of ticks. They stood in silence in the shade and chewed their cud. As they bounded away, their white tails flagged farewell.

The rabbits that had raised their young in fur-lined nests beneath the tree followed the procession of the deer. With long ears flopping, they hopped by, waving upturned cotton tufts of tails.

The rabbits all were safely away before the foxes arrived. There would be no bloodshed on this festive day. The foxes gave their warning barks as they approached, and as each male passed the tree, he "lifted a leg," as he had always done, and left a token of his maleness there, an offering to the oak.

Suspense was added when the skunks arrived. All of them that had ever dug among the roots for grubs and worms and suckling mice joined the pageant. They arrived with adults in the lead and, in single file, the young walking behind. They walked with their noses close to the earth and plumed tails erect and, keeping scent glands tightly shut, moved their tails in a proper greeting.

The mice, the shrews, the moles, the little things that had tunneled through the roots and grass, circled around the base of the tree. They formed a squealing mat of fur, mottled with gray and black and shades of brown.

The earthworms also had their turn: the eyeless creatures who had toiled in silence through the years, digesting leaves and aerating the soil that fed the oak. They showed themselves above the ground and, stretching from hole to hole, entwined about each other in the mating act. This is the most dramatic gesture worms can make.

And while all these passed in parade, the raccoons lay along the limbs, spectators.

Next on the pageant program was the brilliance of fall. For this the leaves changed to their festive garb. Suddenly all of them broke loose in a shower of sunset color and, weaving in and out of the limbs as though executing a dance routine, floated silently down to earth to lie, leaf upon leaf, around the tree that gave them birth.

There was an *in memoriam* for the passenger pigeon, a bird that fed on acorns and now is extinct because of the greed of man. They circled high above the tree, transparent apparitions, making no sound with either throat or wing. Then silently, as they had come, they vanished into the western sky, and night approached.

Next came a backdrop of the sunsets, the finest of them gathered in one great mosaic. Then as it grew dark, the fireflies rose out of the earth. The flashes of their mating calls lit up the tree. They were joined by the crickets and the katydids. Sound competed with the lights, as they "bowed" their legs against their sides in an orchestra of massed violins.

The locusts crawled up the oak as pupae from holes in the ground. There were six cycles of seventeen years condensed in one. After they had emerged, they sang their songs with wings and left their golden pupal shells fastened to the oak as mementos that they had paid their call.

The owls arrived on muted wings and took their places on the bare branches. As the full moon rose, they turned and faced it. A thousand moons were reflected from the depths of their dark, lustrous eyes. Then each gave vent to its peculiar cry, the horned, the barred, the screech. The blended sound became a mournful dirge for the departed nights they had spent in the oak.

The stars shone down just as they had upon the acorn that grew into the towering majesty of the tree. They filled the heavens with concentric circles of celestial light, as each star followed its destined path. The steel-blue brilliance of the small circle created by the North Star on its nocturnal trip became a fitting halo for the oak.

The pageant would take much time. But who am I to meter time and cut short the homage to the oak that grew upon the sloping hillside decades before the seed that produced me felt the touch of life?